639.1173574 SCO.

TABLE OF CONTENTS

ACKNOWLEDGEMENTS

The background work and preparation of this Report was undertaken by an SNH Red Deer Working Group chaired by Lord Strathnaver (NW Regional Board), with Dr Peter Reynolds (Research and Advisory Services Directorate (RASD)) as Technical Secretary; its other members were Nicholas Gubbins (Policy Directorate), Alan Hampson (RASD), David Laird (Chairman, NE Regional Board), Dr Bill Mutch (Chairman, SE Regional Board), Professor Brian Staines (NE Regional Board) and Dr Des Thompson (RASD).

SNH is grateful for the substantial effort and thinking put in by the Working Group in helping SNH to review the whole range of background information and to develop its policies.

SNH also wishes to record its gratitude to the following for their help:
David Balharry, Species Conservation (Animals), RASD, SNH
Dick Balharry, Strathspey Area Manager, NE Region, SNH
Tim Clifford, Reserve Manager, Beinn Eighe & Loch Maree Islands NNRs, NW Region, SNH
Prof. Tim Clutton-Brock FRS, Reader, University of Cambridge
Richard Cooke, Secretary, Association of Deer Management Groups
Dr Robin Gill, Wildlife and Conservation Research Branch, Forestry Authority
Dr Peter Hudson, Manager, Uplands Research Unit, Game Conservancy
Sir John Lister-Kaye, Chairman, NW Regional Board, SNH
Kerry Keysall, Managing Director, Highland Venison Market Ltd
Colin McLean, Deer Officer, Red Deer Commission
Dr Phil Ratcliffe, Head of Wildlife and Conservation Research Branch, Forestry Commission
Russell Turner, Head of Advisory Services, NW Region, SNH
Dr Adam Watson, Former Senior Principal Scientific Officer, ITE, Banchory
Dr Jeff Watson, Head of Land Management, NW Region, SNH
Dick Youngson, Senior Deer Officer, Red Deer Commission.

RED DEER AND THE NATURAL HERITAGE:

SNH Policy Paper

Preface: Magnus Magnusson

'These creatures are more than the material of the scientist's paper. They are animals whose lot has been closely linked with human development. We have pitted our wits against them through thousands of years and the hunter is not worth his salt who does not admire this quarry and is not content sometimes to watch the beauty of their lives, free from the desire to kill.'

(Frank Fraser Darling: A Herd of Red Deer, 1937)

Scotland's natural heritage embraces the land and all its wildlife resources. Red deer are an intrinsic part of that natural heritage, and they depend for their survival upon the health of the habitats within the deer range. However, human management has conspired with natural conditions to favour the very considerable expansion of red deer numbers. These factors, together with much burning of habitat and heavy grazing by sheep, have contributed to a marked deterioration in the quality of our upland environment.

There is an urgent need for a fresh appraisal of the way in which we manage our red deer to ensure that both deer and those elements of the natural heritage on which they depend are sustained in a balanced and healthy state. Viable populations must be conserved, but if we are to achieve our vision of an upland environment which is diverse in terms of the landscapes, wildlife and human activities which it supports, then radical changes are required. The important issue of public access to open hill country during the shooting season is being addressed in a forthcoming SNH policy paper on Access in Scotland.

In broad terms, the restoration of the native woodland ecosystem is at the very heart of our vision for the uplands. Today this ecosystem, perhaps more than any other, reflects the adverse effects of inappropriate management for red deer and sheep. In the central and east Highlands the restoration of major tracts of native woodland, with all its constituents of open and closed canopy, water bodies, diverse shrub and ground-cover vegetation must be a high priority. In the west, where the remaining fragments of native woodland are more scattered and interspersed with important areas of open wet heath and bog, woodland restoration at a more local scale is envisaged. We see red deer as an integral part of these regenerating woodlands, albeit at reduced densities.

SNH bases its thinking on three guiding principles:

* First, we regard red deer as an integral part of the environment. The sight of Britain's largest wild mammal is a source of great pleasure to many visitors and is thus a part of the broader tapestry which provides the basis for the tourism industry. We respect the cultural and economic importance of red deer to many small but important rural communities in Scotland.

* Secondly, we view the red deer population as a resource requiring sustainable management.

* Thirdly, and most critically, our overall objective is to see the improvement of countryside quality measured in terms of the enhanced biodiversity and productivity of the natural heritage within the deer range. While the restoration of native woodland is fundamental in this respect, we also recognise the importance of maintaining the open habitats below the tree-line, such as heather moorland and boglands, which characterise the wilder uplands of Scotland.

In this Policy Paper, SNH sets out its policies for securing a sustainable balance through focused research and demonstration projects. In doing so, we recognise that management of red deer per se cannot be considered in isolation from that of the habitats on which they depend, and that our own role in most respects will be advisory. Statutory responsibility rests with the Red Deer Commission; we support the RDC's role and would like to see it substantially strengthened, as we said in our Response to the Government's Consultation Paper on Deer Legislation in Scotland (December 1991). Primary responsibility for the stewardship of red deer and their range, however, rests with the owners and managers of the land; their role is therefore critical in ensuring the future health of the deer and their balance with the habitat. SNH believes that this is best fostered through the voluntary groupings of Deer Management Groups (DMGs), and we intend to work closely with them, both through membership of individual DMGs and as an advisor on natural heritage matters.

Magnus Magnusson KBE
Chairman, Scottish Natural Heritage

June 1994

PART 1: BACKGROUND

HISTORICAL BACKGROUND

Agriculture and sport

The management of wild red deer *Cervus elaphus* in Scotland has been a contentious issue for some 200 years. Between 1872 and 1954 no fewer than seven Government-appointed enquiries were established to address the issues.

In the early days of the debate, attention was focused on the relationship between agriculture and the management of red deer for sport. Five Government enquiries considered this aspect of the red deer conflict during the period 1870-1920, three of which were concerned with deer damage to agricultural land and two with increased use of deer forest for agricultural occupation, cultivation and grazing. Relevant legislation was not enacted until 1948 with the passage of the Agriculture (Scotland) Act which granted the right of occupiers of agricultural holdings to kill deer marauding on enclosed land.

Forestry

With the expansion of plantation forestry following the establishment of the Forestry Commission in 1919, the red deer conflict was set to take on a new dimension, although the problems did not manifest themselves until the early 1950s. By this time it was apparent that red deer and plantation forestry were competing directly for land (e.g. RDC Annual Report 1960).

The management of wild red deer in Scotland has been a contentious issue for some 200 years.

Objective counts

Red deer numbers probably declined between c.1939 and 1950, partly in response to increased shooting and poaching (Staines & Ratcliffe 1987; Callander & MacKenzie 1991). In the post-war years there was increasing interest in the assessment of the number of red deer in the Highlands. As a consequence, in 1952 Frank Fraser Darling was appointed by the Nature Conservancy to survey the Scottish deer population, and the first counts of the survey were initiated in 1953.

Deer (Scotland) Act 1959

At the same time, attempts were made to introduce legislation enforcing close seasons and increasing penalties for poaching, culminating in the Deer (Scotland) Act 1959. This Act, as amended, continues to provide the basic framework for the management of wild red deer in Scotland.

Red Deer Commission

Among the provisions of the Act were the definition of legal close seasons and the establishment of the Red Deer Commission with overall responsibility for the conservation and control of wild red deer in Scotland. From its inception the RDC has argued for a reduction in the red deer population.

Deer Management Groups

The emergence of Deer Management Groups, particularly over the last 10 years, has been one of the key features in the recent history of red deer management. These groups, the first of which was formed in 1963, have voluntary membership and promote information exchange and co-ordinated deer management. 45 Deer Management Groups now exist, covering nearly all the traditional red deer range in Scotland.

Red deer populations transcend individual ownership boundaries. Deer Management Groups constitute biologically realistic units of management because each covers an area which should correspond to a more or less distinct sub-population of deer.

Natural heritage

The origins of the natural heritage dimension to the red deer debate go back to the early 1900s. Ritchie (1920) expressed concern that numbers in many areas exceeded the carrying capacity of the ground, while Seton Gordon (1925) drew attention to the lack of natural regeneration in the native pinewoods of upper Deeside due to grazing by red deer. These fears were subsequently echoed by Fraser Darling (1955) who argued that a reduction in population would benefit not just the habitat but also the deer stock. All these commentators were writing at a time when red deer populations were substantially lower than they are today.

These expressions of concern that red deer were having an adverse impact on the natural heritage appeared to carry little weight. No account appears to have been taken of them in the drafting of the Deer (Scotland) Act 1959, which was concerned primarily with the protection of agriculture and forestry interests and of the deer themselves.

Within the last 20 years the red deer debate has matured in the sense that the problem is now increasingly being articulated in terms of the need for a more integrated approach to the management of red deer. It is within this context and within this time period that the natural heritage element of the debate has developed. Key publications in this respect include McVean & Lockie (1969), Lowe (1969, 1971), Mutch et al. (1976), Mitchell et al. (1977), Clutton-Brock & Albon (1989) and the Red Deer Commission Annual Reports (1961-1991). Callander & MacKenzie (1991) and the Cairngorms Working Party Report (1993) all emphasise the need for an integrated approach to red deer management.

Legislative review

In May 1990 the Government produced its response to the Agriculture Select Committee Report, *Land Use and Forestry*, in which it undertook to consider the need for legislative changes to improve the management of wild red deer in Scotland. Subsequently, in December 1991, the Government issued a consultation paper on revised deer legislation which was widely circulated and which has promoted continuing debate. In February 1993 the Red Deer Commission, in response to a request from Government, established a Working Party to draft specific proposals for inclusion in new deer legislation.

RED DEER AS
A RESOURCE

ECOLOGICAL CONTEXT

Red deer are our largest native herbivores and have been present in Scotland since at least the end of the last Ice Age, c.11,000 years ago. They are therefore an integral part of the post-glacial upland ecosystems which we see in Scotland today.

Population decline & range contraction

Red deer were formerly abundant in the extensive woodlands which covered most of Scotland but their range began to contract c.5000 years ago due to forest clearance by man. Historical evidence (e.g.Ritchie 1920) suggests that the red deer range continued to contract thereafter due to forest clearance for agriculture, hunting and the introduction of sheep on hill grazings.

During the 16th century, no fewer than 11 Acts were concerned with the penalties prescribed for the illegal killing of deer. While these Acts may have had more to do with the preservation of hunting as a royal prerogative than with conservation, they may have reflected the declining status of the red deer population. Ritchie (1920) speculated that but for the protection afforded by these Acts, red deer would long since have ceased to exist in Scotland, suffering the same fate as moose *Alces alces*, reindeer *Rangifer tarandus* and red deer in Wales and most of England, where both habitat loss and hunting contributed to extinction.

The low point for red deer populations in Scotland was probably reached in the mid to late 1700s (Cameron 1923). Numbers increased thereafter as deer-stalking became fashionable and sheep farming became less profitable. Large areas of land were specifically devoted to increasing the red deer population for hunting and these "deer forests" nearly doubled in total extent from c.800,000ha in 1883 to over 1.5m ha in 1912 (Callander & MacKenzie 1991).

Population increase & range expansion

Objective counts, initiated by Fraser Darling in 1953 and undertaken subsequently by the Red Deer Commission, indicate that the population has increased from c.150,000 animals in the early 1960s to c.300,000 today **(Table 1)**. For Red Deer Commission counting blocks in which repeat counts have been undertaken, the percentage increases have ranged from c.11% to c.150%. Over this period sequences of mild winters and dry summers, substantial declines in sheep numbers and under-culling of hinds are all factors which have probably assisted the population increase (Clutton-

FIGURE 1. Contemporary distribution of red deer in Scotland.

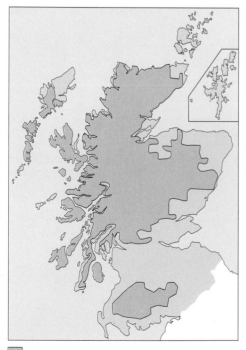

RED DEER DISTRIBUTION

Brock & Albon 1989). Watson (1989) considered that through their browsing, dunging and trampling and the consequent replacement of heather by palatable grasses, red deer may have increased the carrying capacity of their habitat, promoting an increase in numbers.

TABLE 1. Estimated numbers of red deer in Scotland.
Objective counts were implemented in 1953. Up to 1970, estimates refer to open-hill populations only. Post-1970 totals include an estimate of deer inhabiting forestry plantations.

YEAR	NUMBER	SOURCE
1900	150,000	Cameron 1923
1930	250,000	Parnell 1932
1939	200,00	HMSO 1951
1950	100,000	HMSO 1951
1959	155,000	Lowe 1961
1963	150,000+	RDC 1964
1965	180,000	Stewart 1979
1969	185,000	RDC 1989
1970	185,000	RDC 1971
1974	200,000	RDC 1975
1975	270,000	Stewart 1985
1977	255,000	RDC 1989
1979	255,000	RDC 1989
1986	290,000	RDC 1989
1989	300,000	RDC 1989

The red deer range now occupies c.3m ha, or more than 40%, of the land area of Scotland **(Fig. 1)**. The increases documented above have involved both expansions of range and increases in density, although the latter are very variable, ranging from fewer than five deer per square kilometre to over 30. Winter densities, when deer concentrate in preferred areas, can be very much higher. These variations in density probably reflect spatial differences in environmental quality, the extent of competition with sheep and the variation in culling rates (Clutton-Brock & Albon 1989).

The culling of animals for sport or for management purposes is a significant factor in red deer ecology. While the total annual cull has increased substantially, culling rates, particularly of hinds have been insufficient prevent an increase in the red deer population.

European context

In a European context Scotland has by far the largest population of red deer, with an estimated 28% of the European total (Gill 1990). Furthermore, c.80% of the Scottish red deer population now lives in open-hill habitats year-round, in contrast to other European populations, most of which are confined to woodland. Scottish red deer have therefore shown a remarkable degree of adaptation to environmental change.

Self-regulation

Although the red deer population in Scotland has been increasing since the turn of the century, there is little evidence that increased densities have been associated with instability in the form of population peaks and crashes such as those seen in Soay sheep *Ovis aries* populations (Clutton-Brock et al. 1991). On the contrary, it appears that natural changes in fecundity and juvenile survival can limit population size (Mitchell et al.1977; Clutton-Brock & Albon 1989). This density-dependence, which affects most aspects of red deer reproduction, survival and growth, has an important bearing on sustainable harvesting strategies.

Culling

The culling of animals for sport or for management purposes is a significant factor in red deer ecology. In most parts of the Highlands 6%-12% of hinds and between 10%-17% of stags are killed each year (Clutton-Brock & Albon 1989).

Throughout much of Scotland the number of hinds culled is lower than the rate of recruitment. Thus, in 1986 more than 75% of the RDC counting blocks were culling fewer hinds than the number of animals recruited each year (Clutton-Brock & Albon 1989).

While the total annual cull has increased substantially from c.24,000 animals in 1973 to c.70,000 in 1992/3, culling rates, particularly of hinds, have been insufficient to prevent an increase in the red deer population (**Figure 2, Figure 3**). However, the RDC considers that hind culls in 1988/89, 1989/90 and 1990/91 have approximately equalled annual recruitment for the first time. Concentration of stalking effort on stags, as well as the Victorian tradition of retaining high hind numbers in the mistaken belief that this is needed to attract stags, have contributed in large part to the increasingly female-biased contemporary deer population. The fact that some deer managers also derive considerable aesthetic pleasure from the sight of large herds of deer is also likely to have contributed to the population increase.

FIGURE 2. Numbers of red deer shot annually in Scotland (from estate returns; RDC annual reports).

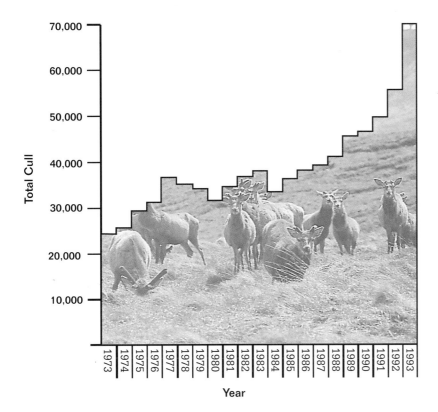

Carrying capacity & performance

With respect to wild red deer in Scotland it is not clear to what extent the population is approaching ecological carrying capacity (ie. the point where the rate of forage production equals the rate of consumption and where birth rates equal death rates). The extent to which further increases in population are possible in the absence of higher culling rates is therefore unknown. That the current population is being influenced by density-dependent factors is, however, evident from the knowledge that individual open hill deer are not achieving their full potential in terms of growth and reproductive output (Mitchell et al. 1977; Staines 1978; Albon et al. 1983; Clutton-Brock & Albon 1989, 1992).

FIGURE 3. Numbers of red deer shot annually in Scotland. Data from estate returns published in RDC annual reports. No data for calves 1973 to 1980.

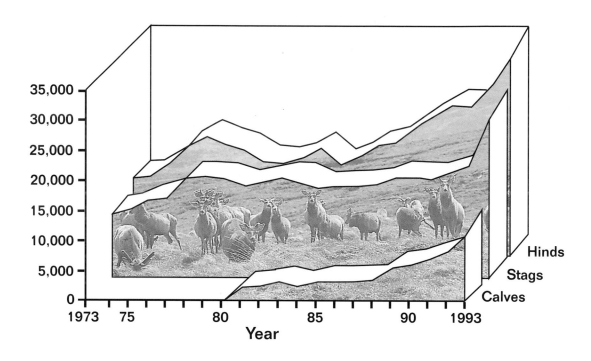

Population density and fecundity have been shown to be inversely related, with both the age of first breeding and the proportion of milk-hinds calving declining with increasing density **(Figure 4)**. As population density increased in the North Block of Rum, the proportion of two-year-old pregnant hinds declined from 65% to 10% and pregnant milk hinds from 90% to 30%. Similar results were recorded with respect to milk hinds at Glenfeshie, where fecundity fell from 80% to 30% as hind numbers increased from 900 to 1200 (Albon 1983). On most Highland deer forests, pregnant yearlings are seldom seen, with the majority of hinds conceiving for the first time as two- or three-year-olds.

Mortality during the first and second winters of life also appears to be density-dependent, and increases with population density, especially in stag calves (Clutton-Brock & Albon 1989) **(Figure 5)**.

High population density affects the survival of juvenile males more than that of females.

FIGURE 4. Changes in the percentage of milk hinds which produced calves as hind density increased in the North Block of Rum. Increasing density was associated with reduced milk-hind calving rates. (Adapted from Clutton-Brock & Albon 1989)

Effects of density on calving rates

FIGURE 5. Mortality during the first two years of life among males and females in the red deer population of the North Block of Rum. High population density affects the survival of males more than that of females. (Adapted from Clutton-Brock & Albon)

Density & juvenile mortality

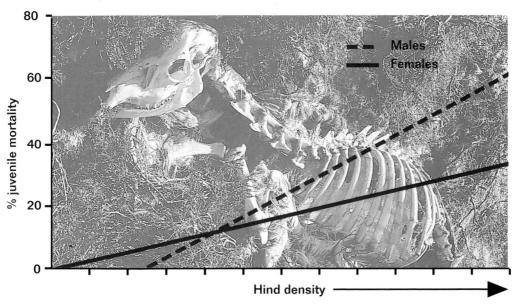

12

FIGURE 6. The median weight of single cast antlers of 7-year-old stags the North Block of Rum in relation to hind density. Antler weight declined as the hind population increased. (Adapted from Clutton-Brock & Albon 1989)

Antler weight and hind density

High population densities have been shown to inhibit post-natal growth. Both antler-length of yearlings and antler-weight in adults have been shown to be inversely correlated with population density (Clutton-Brock & Albon 1989) **(Figure 6)**.

Research on the effects of increasing population density shows, therefore, that most aspects of red deer reproduction, survival and growth decline as density increases.

In addition to density *per se*, habitat can have a dramatic effect on red deer population dynamics and condition **(Figure 7)**. Red deer in woodland habitat, for example, can achieve higher growth rates, higher adult body weights, larger antlers and superior reproductive performance compared with red deer on the open hill (Mitchell et al. 1977, 1981; Ratcliffe 1984; Clutton-Brock & Albon 1989).

Red deer in woodland habitat can achieve higher growth rates, higher adult body weights, larger antlers and superior reproductive performance compared with red deer on the open hill.

7. Fertility of yearling red deer in Scottish & continental
populations in relation to habitat. Note that for a given density,
fertility rates are consistently higher in forest living populations
than in those inhabiting the open hill. (Adapted from Clutton-
Brock & Albon 1989)

Density & juvenile mortality

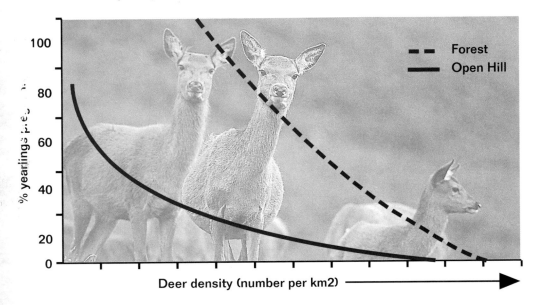

Red deer as part of upland ecosystems : open habitats

Red deer have adapted to the open habitats which now dominate much of the Scottish uplands through a reduction in body size, growth rates and reproductive output (Ritchie 1920; Lowe 1961; Youngson 1970; Arman 1971; Blaxter et al. 1974; Mitchell et al. 1977; Clutton-Brock & Albon 1989).

Within these open habitats much of the diet is provided by grasses and dwarf shrubs, especially heather *Calluna vulgaris*, which is important in winter (Staines 1970; Colquhoun 1971; Mitchell et al. 1977; Staines et al. 1978; Staines & Crisp 1978). Red deer can be selective in their choice of food (Holloway 1967; Welch 1971) and selection may be influenced by the combination of species available. Staines (1970), for example, found that heather was more heavily browsed when in association with blaeberry *Vaccinium myrtillus* and wavy-hair grass *Deschampsia flexuosa* than when in pure stands.

Red deer tend to utilise the same plant species as sheep, although as body weight increases there is an overall decrease in the use of plant communities of medium nutrient status *Agrostis-Festuca* associations and *Juncus* marsh and an overall increase in the use of nutrient poor communities *Calluna-Trichophorum* moor, *Molinia* and *Nardus* grassland (Hobson et al. 1976; Osborne 1984; Gordon 1989). Sheep grazing can maintain plant species diversity, at least in some communities (Marrs & Welch 1991), and it seems reasonable to suggest therefore that grazing by red deer at moderate densities may promote the maintenance, development and perhaps spread of species-rich swards (Watson 1989). That grazing by red deer at high densities may be detrimental to species-rich swards, however, is indicated by a review of long term floristic changes over 34 years on Rum (Ball *in prep*). Ball concludes that where the red deer population has been allowed to increase in the absence of culling, 14 plant species have been lost or have drastically declined.

Red deer have adapted to the open habitats which now dominate much of the Scottish uplands through a reduction in body size, growth rates and reproductive output.

The role of red deer in the maintenance of heather moorland is ambiguous. Mitchell et al. (1977), writing at a time when the red deer population was c.30,000 less than today, argued that stocking the uplands exclusively with deer would bring about a reversion of grasslands to dwarf-shrub heath. They supported their contention on the basis that red deer, in contrast to sheep, occupy their range more evenly, eat a higher proportion of *Calluna* and a lower proportion of grass than sheep on the same ground, and prefer to graze grassy *Calluna* rather than pure *Agrostis-Festuca* grassland. Some contemporary authorities (eg. Watson 1989) take a contrary view and consider that high deer numbers are causing a shift from dwarf-shrub heath to grassland. While circumstantial evidence suggests that deer-induced heather-loss is taking place, there is clearly a need for more information on the precise respective roles of sheep, red deer and other herbivores in influencing vegetation dynamics in the uplands.

Whatever the precise nature of the dynamic relationship between red deer and vegetation, it is likely that these animals contribute to the maintenance of the open habitats which many people, including ecologists, value as an important component of the uplands of Scotland. Such open habitats favour bird species of high conservation value such as golden plover *Pluvialis apricaria* and dunlin *Calidris alpina*.

Red deer as part of upland ecosystems : woodland habitats

Woodlands in the uplands can benefit from light grazing by large herbivores such as red deer. These animals can produce and maintain structural and species diversity, both in terms of plant communities and dependent woodland faunas. In addition, ground disturbance by grazing animals creates niches for tree seedling establishment (Mitchell & Kirby 1990; Sykes 1992).

Red deer as a source of carrion

Red deer also provide a source of food for a variety of upland vertebrates. The diet of golden eagles *Aquila chrysaetos* in winter over much of their range in Scotland is predominantly carrion in the form of sheep and deer (Watson,J.et al.1987; Watson,J. et al. in press). Brown & Watson (1964) concluded that the nesting density of eagles in Scotland was not linked to overall food supply. Their data were subsequently reinterpreted to suggest that densities were higher where live prey alone was more plentiful (Newton 1979; Tjernberg 1983). More recently, however, Watson,J. et al.(1992) have concluded that the nesting density of these birds is correlated with the supply of sheep and deer carrion, while breeding success is dependent on the amount of live prey in the form of grouse *Lagopus lagopus* & *Lagopus mutus*, hares *Lepus timidus* and rabbits *Oryctolagus cuniculus*. They further suggest that the amount of food available in winter, notably carrion, may be the single most important factor determining the number of pairs which a given area can support. A decline in the density of golden eagles in a part of the east Highlands since the early 1960s was attributed to a reduction in red deer mortality and a consequent reduction in carrion availability (Watson,J.et al.1989).

Woodlands in the uplands can benefit from light grazing by large herbivores such as red deer.

Red deer provide a source of carrion for species such as the golden eagle.

Other upland birds feeding on red deer carrion include raven *Corvus corax*, crow *Corvus corone* and buzzard *Buteo buteo* (Cramp et al.1980).

Red deer carrion occurs in the diet of the red fox *Vulpes vulpes* (Lockie 1963, 1964; Watson 1976; Hewson 1983) and has also been recorded in the diet of badgers *Meles meles* (Hewson & Kolb 1976). In a study of pine martens *Martes martes* at Strathglass, Balharry (1993) found that carrion comprised 31% of the estimated annual food intake by weight and that 99% of this comprised deer carrion. Corresponding figures for his second study area at Kinlochewe were 41% and 79% respectively. Red deer carrion is also likely to be of importance for a range of invertebrates.

AESTHETIC CONTEXT

It is clear that many people derive considerable pleasure from wild red deer. The occurrence of a large native herbivore which can be seen in herds provides an experience unique within the British Isles and one which is profoundly enjoyed by visitors and stalkers alike. On the other hand, by contributing to the demise of native woodlands, these same animals are promoting the loss of an important element in the upland landscapes from which people also derive considerable pleasure.

SPORTING CONTEXT

Deer drives

Red deer have been hunted since Mesolithic settlers first colonised Scotland after the end of the last Ice Age. During the medieval period large-scale deer drives were undertaken and kills of up to 300 animals in a day are recorded (Ritchie 1920; Lowe 1961). This method of hunting continued until the end of the 18th century and, together with the loss of forest habitat and competition with sheep, contributed to the probable nadir of the red deer population in Scotland in the mid to late 1700s.

Evolution of stalking

Contemporary stalking methods originated in the mid 19th century, in response to a combination of circumstances including increased wealth (generated outwith the Highlands), developments in sporting firearms and social fashion. As a consequence, estates were purchased by wealthy individuals and much of the estate infrastructure which we see today in the form of roads, bridges and shooting lodges was established. In contrast to the hunting methods of previous centuries, in which deer were driven, stalking was and continues to be highly selective, with the emphasis almost entirely on stags.

Commercial significance: stalking

Contemporary deer forests devoted to stalking cover c.l.5m ha (c.19% of the land area of Scotland). The only study to address specifically the economics of the red deer industry is that of Jarvie (1979), in which it was suggested that sporting estates were seldom profitable. More recently, the Fraser of Allander Institute (1990) studied the economics of sport shooting but did not separate red deer from other quarry in most instances. Nevertheless their findings confirmed Jarvie's earlier claims. On the basis of Jarvie's study, Callander & MacKenzie (1991) suggested that only c.16% of all deer killed (c.31% of stags and c.3% of hinds) are shot on a commercial let basis, providing an income from commercial lets in the region of c.£1.5-2m per annum (based on average fees of c.£200-£250 for open hill stags and c.£50 for hinds).

Stalking is highly selective with the emphasis on stags.

Commercial significance : venison

Venison production has increased since 1969 from c.1,500 tons per annum to c.2,500 tons in 1992/93. Although income from this source increased from £0.5m in 1969 to more than £3m in 1989, the slump in prices experienced in 1990/91 (£1.3m) illustrates the fickle state of the industry, which is dependent on European markets. In 1992/93 income from venison increased to c.£6m (data from Highland Venison Ltd., based on 1992 cull of 70,000 animals, average carcase weight of 32.25kg and price of £2.33 per kg).

More recently, attempts have been made to develop the home market for wild venison shot for sporting/management purposes. The Argyll Group began marketing wild venison in selected branches of the Safeways supermarket chain in January 1993 and in the first season of operation purchased 2,000 carcases, equivalent to c.3% of the 1992/93 cull. During the 1993/94 season Safeways anticipate purchasing c.15% of the total cull.

Close seasons

For the purposes of venison production the existing stag and hind stalking seasons (1 July-20 October and 21 October-15 February respectively) are not ideal. Many of the stags are shot during the rut, when their condition is declining, and hinds shot in the latter half of the season tend to be in relatively poor condition.

From a welfare point of view, however, the existing stag season is conducive to humane culling: during the rut, stags tend to occur in smaller groups and are therefore easier to shoot than at other times of year.

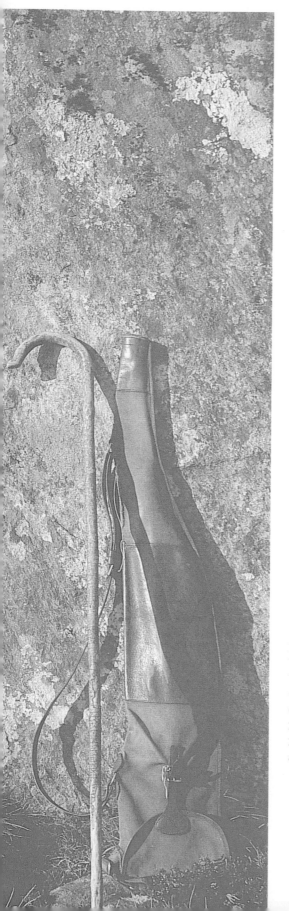

Close seasons were introduced in 1962 following provisions in the Deer (Scotland) Act 1959 and were introduced primarily as a deterrent to poaching, with welfare aspects a secondary consideration (HMSO 1954). It is questionable whether or not there is a case for close seasons in red deer under contemporary conditions.

Employment

Estates involved in the management of red deer make local contributions to rural employment and the maintenance of rural communities, although the number of staff involved has declined this century, despite increasing deer populations. Jarvie (1979) estimated direct employment on estates associated with red deer management to be 570 people full time and 300 temporary staff. The Red Deer Commission currently estimates 316 permanent and 458 part-time staff to be involved with red deer management, reflecting the trend from full to part-time employment and the seasonal nature of the culls (Callander & MacKenzie 1991).

In addition to the direct employment associated with red deer management, various down-stream activities also contribute to rural employment. For example, Jarvie (1979) estimated 173 full time job equivalents for these other sectors of the deer industry, although this figure is generally considered to be conservative.

While red deer stalking and venison sales generate significant economic activity, red deer management by estates appears seldom to be profitable and to be dominated by non-economic factors (Jarvie 1979; Fraser of Allander Institute 1990). This is reflected in the fact that c.40% of estates did not let any stalking commercially (Jarvie 1979). Many estates thus subsidise sporting activities and employment using finance generated elsewhere.

Stalking procedure

Traditional stalking involves locating individual animals on foot and attaining a position from which the quarry can be humanely and cleanly shot. The carcase is then carried by pony, or physically dragged by the stalker, to a point where it can be uplifted by vehicle or boat to the estate larder. Stalking, when undertaken conscientiously, is thus a skilful and physically demanding activity. On some estates, stalkers and their shooting clients are transported by all-terrain vehicles (ATVs) and these may also be used to remove culled animals. The use of ATVs is increasing on some estates and in some situations these vehicles are having an adverse effect on vegetation and soils.

Selective shooting : stags

Traditionally, stalking has been directed at large and mature stags between 7 and 10 years old with antlers of good size and shape, or at stags considered to have unfavourable characteristics. The latter has been undertaken in the hope of improving stock and, although there is some evidence that antler shape may be genetically determined (Ahlèn 1965), the role of environment would also seem to be important in influencing some aspects of antler development. For example, Clutton-Brock & Albon (1989) present convincing data which show that antler length and weight are influenced by hind density. This being the case, selective shooting may have little effect, at least with respect to the determination of ultimate antler size.

Selective shooting : hinds

Hinds are rarely culled for sport. Most are taken by estate staff for stock management. Precisely which hinds should be culled is a matter of debate. The selection of animals with poor calves may help to eliminate poor breeders from the population and may help to reduce calf mortality in winter. The selective culling of old hinds has also been advocated, on the basis that reproductive performance and survival will be enhanced. However, a hind's chance of surviving the winter and of breeding successfully the following year do not appear to deteriorate until she is over 13 years old, and only a small proportion of animals will reach this age in a culled population (Mitchell et al.1977; Clutton-Brock & Albon 1989). However, in woodland habitats poor visibility and generally good hind condition conspire to make selective culling difficult.

Removing a culled red deer from the hill. Over 300 permanent and 400 part-time staff are estimated to be involved directly with red deer management on upland estates in Scotland.

THREATS TO THE RED DEER RESOURCE

Genetic isolation

Scotland's native wild red deer are the descendants of red deer which became re-established in Britain c.11,000 years ago following the end of the last Ice Age and before the land-bridge to Europe became submerged. Contemporary populations have therefore been genetically isolated for a considerable time and have either been regarded as a distinct subspecies *Cervus elaphus scoticus* (Whitehead 1972) or as one extreme of a range of variation which extends eastwards to China (Lowe & Gardiner 1974).

Introductions

Introductions of deer, particularly during the 19th century from England, Europe and North America, threatened the genetic integrity of native red deer in Scotland. These deer were introduced in an attempt to improve the 'quality' of the indigenous stock for sport shooting. These efforts were, however, misguided, given that many of the desired characteristics are environmentally rather than genetically determined (Mitchell et al.1977; Clutton-Brock & Albon 1989).

While these introductions were generally on a small scale, they were widespread geographically (Whitehead 1964). It is known that the red deer of Galloway are likely to have descended from feral deer which escaped during the Second World War and that the deer on Rum and South Uist have also been introduced using non-native stock (Callander & MacKenzie 1991).

In the absence of detailed genetic studies it is impossible to assess the extent to which the genotypes of our indigenous red deer have been diluted or to identify genetic refuges of *Cervus elaphus scoticus*.

Escapes from deer farms, of which there are about 70 in Scotland with a stock of c.18,500 animals (Callander & MacKenzie 1991), also threaten the genetic integrity and health of native wild stocks. While many of the animals reared on deer farms will be obtained by the live capture of wild stock, selective breeding is likely to alter the wild genotype, which may be detrimental to native stocks in the event of the inevitable escapes. These escapes also provide a potential means by which disease could be introduced into the wild population - the biggest threat in this respect being the spread of bovine TB, outbreaks of which have already been documented on deer farms (Callander & MacKenzie 1991).

Sika deer

Sika deer *Cervus nippon* pose a serious threat to the genetic integrity of wild red deer stocks. Between 1879 and 1910 these Asiatic deer escaped from several Scottish deer parks and were intentionally released in at least two sites in the Highlands (Ratcliffe 1987). Since 1930, Scottish sika populations have expanded their range considerably and Ratcliffe documents an average rate of colonisation in Argyll of 3-5sq km per year.

Perceptions of the extent of the hybridisation problem are varied. Some authorities maintain that where red deer and sika occur together, both populations may maintain their genetic integrity (Lowe & Gardiner 1975). On the other hand, experience from other areas shows that once hybrids are present, further hybridisation can be rapid. In the southern Lake District of England (Lowe & Gardiner 1975) and the Wicklow Mountains of Ireland (Harrington 1973,1982) the deer populations are now composed almost entirely of red-sika hybrids. It has been suggested by Ratcliffe (1987) that in time pure red deer may only survive on some islands.

Sika deer pose a serious threat to the genetic integrity of wild red deer stocks.

In terms of habitat preference, sika deer typically occur in thickly wooded habitats, including mixed deciduous and coniferous forests. The thicket stages of commercial forests provide a highly suitable environment (Ratcliffe 1987). These are precisely the habitats in which the control and management of deer populations are exceedingly difficult, particularly for a species which is considered to make better use of cover and which is therefore more difficult to control than red deer (Ratcliffe 1987). Following a three-year study in 20-year-old thicket plantation at Shin, in Sutherland, the Red Deer Commission has concluded that control of sika by shooting would require ranger densities of more than one per 200-300ha of plantation. Contemporary ranger densities in Shin Forest are in the region of one per 8,000ha. The manpower implications are therefore formidable and the RDC has concluded that sika control by shooting is impracticable (McLean 1993).

Loss of red deer wintering habitat

Red deer are selective in their use of habitats (Clutton-Brock & Albon 1989); consequently, removal of preferred habitats from their range may have a disproportionate effect on population density or reproductive performance.

In winter, red deer typically select areas of lower ground which offer both grazing (e.g. flushed grasslands) and vitally important shelter. It is estimated that over 300,000 ha of traditional deer wintering grounds were lost between 1959-79 (RDC Annual Report 1981), largely due to afforestation, and this loss continued into the 1980s.

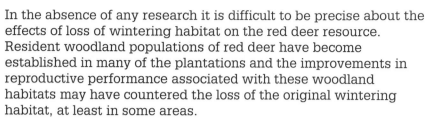

In the absence of any research it is difficult to be precise about the effects of loss of wintering habitat on the red deer resource. Resident woodland populations of red deer have become established in many of the plantations and the improvements in reproductive performance associated with these woodland habitats may have countered the loss of the original wintering habitat, at least in some areas.

Interactions with sheep

Red deer share much of their range with approximately 2 million sheep. Both species share a strong preference for *Agrostis-Festuca* grasslands (Colquhoun 1971; Charles et al.1977; Osborne 1984), and although deer tend to use higher altitude levels and eat proportionately less grass than hill sheep, it would be surprising if competition between the two species did not occur.

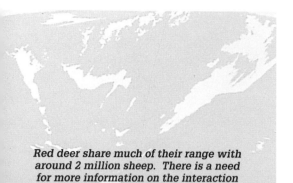

Red deer share much of their range with around 2 million sheep. There is a need for more information on the interaction between these two species.

A comparison between the relative use of different plant communities on Rum (no sheep), and similar ground at one site in Argyll (22 sheep/sq.km), showed that hinds and stags at the latter site spent considerably less time feeding in communities dominated by herbs and *Agrostis-Festuca* grassland (Charles et al.1977; Osborne 1984; Clutton-Brock & Albon 1989). The latter authors also noted a negative correlation between geographical and temporal variations in sheep numbers and deer density. Clutton-Brock & Albon (1992) showed that following a reduction in sheep numbers on particular estates, deer numbers increased. These studies suggest that in some situations sheep may be at a competitive advantage and that where they share range, deer may be excluded from preferred plant communities. Hinds, which tend to exploit short grassy swards more than stags, may be especially vulnerable in this respect (Clutton-Brock & Albon 1989). This may not be the whole story, however. Anecdotal evidence from some areas points to the simultaneous increase of both sheep and deer numbers. In addition, it has been suggested that deer may be unable to maintain areas of preferred *Agrostis-Festuca* grassland in the absence of sheep (Ball 1974; Mitchell et al. 1977). Considered together with the ambiguous roles of sheep and deer as agents of habitat change, the interaction of these two species is clearly an area which merits further research.

Over-population?

From a biological perspective, there would appear to be little evidence to support the view that the red deer population needs to be controlled for its own sake. High populations of lightly culled or unculled animals are not necessarily unstable and there is no evidence that the Scottish red deer population has exceeded the carrying capacity of its habitat. The justification for reducing the population numbers is dictated by the need to protect and enhance elements of the natural heritage. In some areas, rising deer numbers cause the habitat to change to a more productive type of vegetation, such as grassland, which can sustain more deer but contains fewer important or precious elements of our natural heritage.

 RED DEER AS A
SOURCE OF CONFLICT

AGRICULTURE

In terms of the evolution of the 'red deer problem' the conflict with agriculture achieved prominence at a very early stage. During the second half of the 19th century, when both the area of land devoted to deer forests and the deer population were increasing, the conflict became a political issue.

Legislation

During the period 1870-1920 there were five government enquiries associated with the conflict, three of which were concerned with damage to crops caused by marauding deer and two with increased use of deer forests for agricultural purposes. With respect to marauding, the three enquiries were consistent in their recommendations : deer forest owners should be obliged to fence their deer forests where they adjoined cultivated land; agricultural occupiers should have the right to kill marauding deer on enclosed ground; and a government-appointed body should be responsible for reducing deer on unenclosed land where they caused damage. Only the last two of these recommendations were embodied in legislation by the Agriculture (Scotland) Act 1948 (right to kill marauding deer), and the Deer (Scotland) Act 1959 (establishment of the Red Deer Commission).

Agricultural protection cull

Since 1976/77 (the first year for which records allow the calculation to be made) the agricultural protection cull has averaged c.3,500 deer per annum (range 797-6443) (Callander & McKenzie 1991), equivalent to c.7% of the total red deer cull.

It is not known whether the marauding problem has increased with the rising deer population. The Red Deer Commission has reported an increase in the number of complaints by farmers and crofters in recent years, but it is acknowledged that the number of complaints is not necessarily a good measure of the scale of the problem (RDC 1989): complaints may, for example, reflect the state of the venison market rather than the degree of marauding *per se*, with increased venison prices resulting in fewer complaints.

Economic impact of marauding

Surprisingly, the economic impact of marauding by red deer does not appear to have been quantified. In the absence of these data and objective information pertaining to trends in the incidence of marauding, it is difficult to assess the scale of the red deer/ agriculture conflict in terms of crop-damage.

Marauding by stags

As assessed by the proportion of stags (15-30%) and hinds (<10%) killed out of season, stags appear to be the more likely to maraud on agricultural land (Mitchell et al.1977; Callander & McKenzie 1989). The higher energy requirements of stags may force them to seek more profitable feeding areas in terms of food availability (Watson & Staines 1978; Staines, Crisp & Parish 1982; Clutton-Brock & Albon 1989). The killing of marauding stags is a source of frustration for deer managers.

FORESTRY

The seeds of the red deer/forestry conflict were sown in 1919 with the establishment of the Forestry Commission and the associated expansion of plantation forestry in the uplands; however, the problem did not become fully apparent until the 1950s. The practical difficulties of controlling deer in plantation woodlands are considerable.

Loss of wintering ground versus establishment of resident woodland red deer populations

The effects of the spread of this plantation forestry on the red deer population have been equivocal. The area of formerly open habitat available to deer, particularly wintering areas, has been reduced. The consequences for red deer populations in terms of the influence on local numbers, growth and reproductive performance have not been the subject of systematic study. On the other hand, many of the fenced plantations have become porous, and both temporary and resident deer populations have been established. Maintenance of fences after their requirement for forestry purposes has ceased could assist deer management.

Red deer are now resident in most plantations throughout Scotland (Staines & Ratcliffe 1987), with the number of forest-dwelling deer estimated to be between 27,000 (Stewart 1988) and 50,000 (Ratcliffe 1987b) animals. The variation in the estimates reflects the difficulty of assessing deer numbers in plantations. Afforestation improves the habitat for deer by providing more food and shelter. Compared with open-hill deer, forest-dwelling animals are frequently larger and heavier and have improved reproductive performance (Mitchell et al. 1981, Ratcliffe 1987b)

Tree heavily browsed by red deer.

Economic impact

From the forester's perspective, conflicts arise from the damage caused by red deer as a consequence of browsing and bark-stripping. The susceptibility of trees to damage is influenced by such variables as tree species, provenance, tree height/age, type of shoots browsed, site factors and the frequency of browsing (Mitchell et al. 1977, Staines & Welch 1989).

Comprehensive and comparable assessments of the economic costs arising from such damage are lacking, with economic impacts having been estimated in only a few cases. For example, deer damage to forestry in Galloway has been estimated to cost £2m per annum (Allison 1990), while in another instance damage to a 250ha Forestry Commission plantation has been estimated to result in losses of £2000 per hectare (Callander & Mackenzie 1991). It has been suggested from studies of sitka spruce at Glenbranter Forest, Argyll, that in the long term the economic losses may be less than previously feared (Staines & Welch 1984).

Large sums of money are expended in attempts to control the forest deer population. While these costs are to some extent offset by income generated from venison, stalking and trophy charges, the cost of the protection cull is considered greatly to exceed income from shooting in all Scottish forests (RDC 1990). Gill (Forestry Commission: personal communication) has estimated the total cost of red and roe deer control in Forestry Commission plantations in Britain to be in the region of c.£5m, net of revenues from venison and stalking (c.£1.26m). Approximately half this expenditure arises from ranger salaries and fencing costs, while the remainder represents loss of production due to bark-stripping and browsing. To put this cost in context, this loss of income is equivalent to c.6.9% of the total revenue generated by Forestry Commission timber sales in 1989/90.

Forestry protection cull

Records of the annual numbers of red deer culled for the purposes of forest protection are available from 1976. They show an increase in the number culled from c.5,000 to c.6,000 per annum in 1988 (RDC 1989), equivalent to c.12% of the annual red deer cull. Due to the enhanced productivity and lower mortality of woodland red deer (Ratcliffe 1984), attempts to stabilise woodland populations are likely to require relatively high culling rates of c.18-25% (Ratcliffe 1987b).

Forest design & rotations

The design and management of many plantation forests are not conducive to the effective control of red deer populations, with dense plantings and few rides inhibiting shooting. In addition, the relatively short 45-55 year rotations which characterise commercial forests in upland Britain result in relatively high proportions of pre-thicket and thicket stage plantation being available (Ratcliffe et al. 1986). It is at those growth stages that red deer densities are at or near their maximum (Ratcliffe et al. 1986; Staines & Ratcliffe 1987).

Sika expansion

The expansion of commercial forestry is facilitating the spread of sika deer, a species which unlike the red deer is largely confined to wooded habitats. The potential spread of sika/red hybridisation and the implications for the integrity of native stocks of red deer have already been discussed.

NATURAL HERITAGE

Red deer as agents of habitat change

Through grazing and browsing, the increasing population of red deer may be one of the agents of vegetation change in the uplands of Scotland. Because red deer share much of their range with c.2 million sheep, however, it is not always clear to what extent the observed changes are attributable to which species. Furthermore, whether these changes are considered detrimental or not depends on perceptions of which habitats should be conserved.

Native woodlands

Concern that red deer populations are responsible for causing adverse changes to habitats is not new. Seton Gordon (1925) and Fraser Darling (1937,1955) both drew attention to the lack of regeneration in the native woodlands of the uplands, attributing this to excessive browsing of seedlings by red deer and sheep.

Native woodland now covers less than 2% of Scotland. In most of these woodlands, little or no regeneration is taking place due to excessive browsing by red deer and sheep.

Native woodland now covers less than 2% of Scotland and it is the loss of this habitat more than any other which dominates the contemporary debate on deer and the natural heritage. In most of these woodlands little or no regeneration is taking place due to browsing (MacKenzie 1987).

The demise of our remaining native Caledonian Pinewoods is typical of the problem with which we are confronted if we wish to conserve these habitats. Studies by Steven & Carlisle (1959) and Watson (1983) suggest that in many of these woodlands little or no regeneration has taken place, in some cases for over 200 years. Concern has been expressed that the remaining trees are coming to the end of their seed-bearing lives. However, recent evidence from a study of the age structure and viability of the remaining Mar Lodge pinewoods has indicated that ageing may not seriously affect the quantity or quality of seed produced up to at least 300 years of age (Nixon 1992). Barring catastrophe, therefore, some trees at this site may remain productive for a further 100 years. Nevertheless, trees are dying every year. In addition, Nixon noted that the interval between good flowering years may increase with age and that seeds produced by scattered trees are less viable than those produced by trees in denser stands. More generally, genetic variation within the remaining fragments of native woodland in Scotland is likely to be reduced due to lack of regeneration and tree deaths. There is, therefore, little room for complacency.

Attempts have been made to define winter densities of deer at or below which tree regeneration will take place (**Table 2**). Intuitively, Fraser Darling (1937) proposed densities of c.5-6 deer per sq.km or less, and subsequent studies have confirmed his views (Holloway 1967; Cummins & Miller 1982). Our knowledge of the precise relationship between deer density and tree

TABLE 2. Response of tree regeneration to red deer density

WINTER DEER DENSITY km2	SPECIES	RESPONSE	SOURCE
33-50	Scots Pine Birch	regeneration prevented	Cummins & Miller 1982
25	Scots Pine	regeneration prevented	Holloway 1967
6	Various	some regeneration	Darling 1937
4	Scots Pine	some regeneration	Holloway 1967
2	Scots Pine	regeneration	Holloway 1967

**TABLE 3. Preferences for different native tree species by red deer.
From Mitchell et al (1977), Staines & Welch (1989)**

HIGHLY PREFERRED	Salix sp. Populus tremula Fraxinus sp. Corylus sp. Sorbus aucuparia Acer platanoides
PREFERRED	Quercus sp. Fagus sp.
LESS PREFERRED	Pinus sylvestris Carpinus sp. Betula sp. Alnus glutinosa Juniperus sp.

regeneration remains inadequate. However, on the basis of the above figure, contemporary total deer densities, which range from fewer than 5 to over 20 per sq.km, are incompatible with tree regeneration in c.83% of the 29 RDC counting blocks for which data are available (1980 - present).

It should be realised, however, that factors other than deer density will influence both the occurrence and type of regeneration. These include sheep grazing, dense ground cover, altitude, proximity of seed sources, soil conditions and browse preferences **(Table 3)**. Nevertheless, where exclosures have been established near seed sources, tree regeneration frequently occurs, demonstrating the overriding importance of grazing.

Tree density may also play an important role in influencing the impact of grazing by deer. At Inshriach (part of the Cairngorms National Nature Reserve) there appears to be an inverse relationship between damage levels and tree density (Staines et al. 1992). The ratio of seedlings to mouths, rather than the number of mouths per se, appears to be most important. In addition, the availability and quality of alternative vegetation types, and their spatial distribution relative to tree seedlings, may also influence the extent of tree browsing.

The factors influencing the impact of red deer on tree regeneration are complex, therefore, and the simplistic compatible densities given above must be seen in this context.

The potential for tree regeneration and improvements in habitat structure are demonstrated by fenced enclosures.

Information pertaining to the role of red deer in promoting damage to, or loss of plant communities other than native woodland is scarce.

While simple reductions in deer density may not necessarily achieve tree regeneration, there are examples where reductions or exclusion of red deer have been encouraging. At Inshriach the regeneration of pine, birch and juniper has been accelerated by heavy culling and the live capture of hinds (Staines et al. 1992). At Creag Meagaidh NNR good birch and rowan establishment is now being achieved following the removal of c.1000 sheep in 1983 and heavy culling and live capture of red deer since 1986. At this site, red deer densities are now equivalent to c.8 per sq.km. Much of the observed regeneration is associated with formerly suppressed trees, perhaps 20 or more years old, which are now flourishing following the lifting of excessive grazing pressure. It is not yet clear to what extent successful seedling establishment is contributing to regeneration at this site.

The potential for tree regeneration is also demonstrated by localised exclosures such as those at Morrone Birkwood NNR, where exclosure has resulted in dense birch regeneration. However, the exclusion of deer does not always result in tree regeneration, possibly as a consequence of distance from seed source or dense ground cover preventing seedling establishment (Sykes 1992). For a review of the effects of removal of grazing on upland vegetation, see Marrs & Welch (1991). Fencing associated with exclosures may need to be maintained for periods exceeding 20 years before removal (Sykes 1992).

Heather moorland & montane habitats

The loss of heather moorland in Scotland is also causing widespread concern, with a c.18% decline in area having been recorded in the period 1947-1973. The causes of this loss are multiple and include afforestation (c.47%) and conversion to semi-improved and unimproved grassland (c.5% and c.48% respectively)(SNH in press). Given that heather tends to undergo a successional transition to rough grassland under conditions of intermediate to high grazing and burning pressure (Miles 1985), this 48% loss to unimproved grassland perhaps reflects the effects of excessive grazing.

However, it is difficult to differentiate between the relative effects of sheep, red deer and burning as contributors to this succession to grassland. Evidence for the role of red deer as agents of widespread heather loss is inconclusive, although it is apparent that they can promote localised losses. Thus, Watson (1989) gives a general account of heather decline attributed to overgrazing largely by deer in upper Deeside. Welch et al. (1992) reported local declines of heather at Mar Lodge since 1946. They also showed declines in the area of heather on the floor of the main glen at Glen Feshie during the period 1970-1992 from 29% to 22%. The results of this study have to be interpreted with considerable caution, however. At both sites cattle have also been grazed and lime and fertilisers have been applied in localised areas to improve the productivity of the vegetation. Supplementary feeding has also been undertaken in the Mar Lodge area. In addition, both declines and increases in heather extent were noted at Glenfeshie, in areas separated by only one or two kilometres.

In their preliminary study of the effects of wintering red deer on heather moorland, Welch et al. (1992) acknowledge the complexity of deer range dynamics and that factors other than absolute numbers of deer can be important. They also emphasise the need for whole-range studies, in preference to research which concentrates on sites of concentrated deer activity or on areas where heather is growing poorly for other reasons. In the absence of such an approach, losses of heather moor due to deer alone are likely to be exaggerated.

Evidence for the role of red deer as agents of widespread heather loss is inconclusive, although it is apparent that they can promote localised losses.

Wild red deer in Scotland share their range with about 2 million hill sheep with densities ranging from <10 to >200 sheep per square kilometre. On low ground with moderately vigorous heather, densities in excess of c.100-200 sheep per square kilometre may cause heather decline. At higher altitudes this critical density declines to <50 sheep per square kilometre (SNH data). Sheep may also, therefore, have contributed to losses of heather moorland.

There are indications that plant communities other than heather moorland may be susceptible to damage by red deer. Thus, Francis et al. (1991) identified at least 11 additional upland plant communities in this category.

These communities may include species which are nationally rare, some of which have been monitored. Thus, on one reserve it is known that c.58% of *Homogyne alpina* flowers were destroyed by deer in 1989 and 1990 (Francis et al. 1991). Given that the significance of such herbivory on the lifetime reproductive output of this particular plant species is unknown, the impact of deer grazing on the *Homogyne alpina* population can not be accurately assessed but appears high enough to warrant concern.

Looking at the vegetation of the British uplands as a whole, Francis et al. (1991) considered that at least 50% of upland plant communities had suffered significant losses from afforestation, 25% from sheep grazing and agricultural reclamation and 3-5% from recreation and pollution. The equivalent figure for deer was considered to be 8%.

There is a need for whole-range studies of habitat use and impact, which in addition to red deer must include sheep and other herbivores such as rabbits and mountain hares.

Within the uplands of Scotland it is very rare to find localities with altitudinal continuity in near-natural vegetation from woodland through scrub and dwarf-shrub heaths to montane summits. This lack of continuity, structural diversity and probable loss of productivity is likely to reflect the effects of grazing by both sheep and deer.

Information pertaining to the role of red deer in promoting damage to, or loss of, plant communities other than native woodland is therefore scarce, ambiguous and frequently anecdotal and the need for whole-range studies of habitat use and impact is clear. These studies must include sheep, and other herbivores such as rabbits and mountain hares, both in terms of their direct effects on vegetation and their interactions with red deer.

Adverse effects on other animals

There is little evidence that the increasing red deer population is having a direct and adverse effect on other animals. The one exception, perhaps, is the dotterel *Charadrius morinellus*, nests and chicks of which have been trampled in some situations (Francis et al. 1991, SNH, unpublished). While in the short-term such incidents are clearly catastrophic for individual birds, the long-term consequences for the dotterel population in terms of reduced lifetime reproductive success are less clear. In addition it is not known if trampling incidents have increased with the expanding deer population. Some nest trampling has also been attributed to sheep. Dotterel are listed under the EC Directive on the Conservation of Wild Birds and this could have implications for the management of red deer (or sheep) where trampling is shown to be a problem.

Other adverse effects are likely to be indirect in nature, and to be mediated by impacts of deer on vegetation, but here again we are in the realm of speculation, with few unambiguous examples. There is evidence to suggest that the abundance of Lepidoptera larvae in ground layer vegetation beneath woodland declines in the presence of heavy deer and/or sheep grazing; this in turn is thought adversely to affect capercaillie populations through a reduction in food availability for chicks (Baines & Sage 1991).

Soil erosion

Fears that high numbers of deer may increase soil erosion in the uplands have been expressed by Francis et al. (1991). The evidence for increased blanket bog hagging and other types of erosion is, however, again anecdotal and no objective data on the extent are available. There is also a problem of interpretation given that erosion could be a response to a range of interacting influences including climatic change and the actions of herbivores. The relative roles of sheep and deer as promoters of upland erosion are also uncertain. Further studies of soil erosion in the uplands are required.

ESTATE MANAGEMENT : RED DEER

Estates concerned with the management of red deer populations undertake a variety of practices which materially affect natural heritage interests.

Muirburn

Muirburn, in which a proportion of ground is burnt each year, is undertaken on many Highland deer forests in order to remove accumulations of dead vegetation and to stimulate the production of young nutritious growth for grouse, sheep or deer. The burning of small strips on a rotational basis is advocated (but not adhered to in many areas) to ensure that the same patches of ground are not burned too frequently (Red Deer Commission 1981; Phillips et al. 1993). Muirburn is not confined to heather moorland and in some areas, particularly in the West Highlands, areas of purple moor grass *Molinia caerulea* are also burned.

The effects of muirburn on the reproductive performance and growth of red deer have not been the subject of systematic study.

Muirburn can have an important influence on the use by deer of less palatable swards. Following experimental burning of two *Molinia* patches on Rum there was a six- to eighteen-fold increase in the extent to which the areas were grazed by deer in spring and early summer. Although usage tailed off thereafter, grazing intensity was still around twice that on adjacent unburned areas a year later (Miles 1971).

The effects of muirburn on the reproductive performance and growth of red deer have not been the subject of systematic study, although there is a suggestion that fecundity may be higher over areas recently burned. Following the creation of fire breaks on Rum, the fecundity of deer in these areas was maintained, in contrast to deer in adjacent unburned areas where the proportion of animals breeding as two year olds fell from c.64% to 31% (Lowe 1971).

The standard of muirburn on deer forest is often poor and this can be detrimental to deer and other interests. For example, fires which burn too hot, at high altitudes or on steep slopes can retard regeneration of palatable species and increase the risk of soil erosion, as can short burning cycles. In addition, unpalatable grasses such as *Molinia*, and the sedges *Eriophorum* and *Trichophorum*, can spread at the expense of the dwarf shrubs which provide an important part of the winter diet of red deer (McVean & Lockie 1969). The generally large size of burned areas on deer forests, in addition to the problems cited above, is detrimental to red grouse. Muirburn is also incompatible with the regeneration of native woodland, with the possible exception of a single burn at the outset to provide good conditions for seedling establishment.

While examples of poor muirburn practice in the uplands of Scotland are obvious, there appear to be no published accounts of attempts to quantify the scale of the problem in terms of extent and impact.

Supplementary feeding

Supplementary winter feeding of deer is undertaken on many estates although the precise number involved is unknown. Feed is provided in the form of maize, hay, silage, potatoes, turnips, deer cobs or mineral blocks, and feeding is primarily confined to stags, although hinds are also fed in some instances. Winter feeding is undertaken for three reasons: i) to confine deer on the ground to maintain the nucleus of a good resident stock and to discourage marauding on adjacent agricultural and forestry areas; ii) to reduce mortality due to severe weather; and iii) to improve the condition of stock in terms of 'better' heads, weight and calving success (Mitchell et al. 1977; Red Deer Commission 1981).

Much of the food available at winter feeding sites appears to be monopolised by a few dominant individuals, particularly stags. These animals can obtain c.17% of their daily maintenance requirements from supplementary food (Wiersema 1974). While some individuals undoubtedly benefit from this additional source of food, winter feeding may have little effect on average performance or antler growth of stags, or average breeding success of hinds. These dominant animals, many of which are old and probably contribute little to the rut, may in fact be preventing access by younger stags.

It is common practice not to shoot stags receiving supplementary food (providing they can be recognised), in the belief that big stags sire big calves. There is no evidence for this; environmental rather than genetic factors have a bigger effect on growth and body size under Scottish conditions (Clutton-Brock & Albon 1989; Staines et al. 1992).

The effects of supplementary feeding on population density, immigration and emigration have not been the subject of systematic study; however, regular feeding in the North Block on Rum between 1968 and 1972 led to increased immigration of stags into the area (Clutton-Brock & Albon 1989). There is only anecdotal evidence that supplementary feeding prevents deer moving away and marauding. Dunnett (1974,1975) tried to divert deer from particular areas using supplementary feeding, and although stags could be moved temporarily to a new site to feed, they still returned to their traditional resting places. Given that the ability to influence deer movements could be a useful management tool, this is an area which would benefit from further research.

Supplementary winter feeding of deer is undertaken on many estates. The effects on population density, immigration and emigration have not been the subject of systematic study.

It is not clear to what extent supplementary feeding is contributing to the increasing red deer population. This practice does, however, tend to concentrate deer and can cause changes in habitat through trampling and grazing. Localised areas of heather moor, for example, can be converted to habitats dominated by grasses. Such changes have been documented at Glenfeshie and Mar Lodge (Welch et al.1992).

Fertilised grasslands

In addition to supplementary feeding, some estates also fertilise or lime areas of grassland for wintering deer, for example at Glen Lui on the Mar Lodge estate. The fertilised lawns at this site now hold stags well into the summer, and grazing pressure on traditional summer grazings may have been reduced accordingly. Further 'whole range' studies are required to determine the precise consequences of this type of management for the conservation of natural heritage interests.

Fencing

Fencing is commonly used by estates for two different purposes. On the one hand, fencing is used to exclude deer from plantations, while at the other extreme fences may be used to confine deer populations to prevent straying on to adjacent estates and marauding of agricultural land.

As a management tool it can be argued that fencing in isolation is a crude and generally ineffective method of deer management. As far as we are aware, fences for the purposes of confinement are located on the basis of ownership/topographical considerations rather than on known deer herd hefts. It is possible in these circumstances that deer may be prevented from optimal use of their traditional range and that, through confinement, problems associated with elevated grazing levels may be intensified. Similar arguments prevail with respect to fencing associated with plantations, where deer may be excluded from traditional wintering ground or movement between areas may be impeded. There is a need for more objective information on range-use by discrete deer herds in Scotland.

Fencing, when integrated with other methods of deer management, is of benefit in some situations, such as the protection of regenerating native woodland. Under these circumstances, fencing protects trees until a stage of growth and/or density is reached at which they are no longer vulnerable to browsing by deer. Short-term rotational fencing, when used in this way and when integrated with effective culling policies, may be an important method by which native woodland regeneration can be achieved in the uplands of Scotland.

Short-term rotational fencing, when integrated with effective culling policies, may be an important method by which native woodland regeneration can be achieved.

Deer fencing can be visually obtrusive.

Deer fencing is a cause of mortality for woodland gamebirds such as capercaillie *Tetrao urogallus*, black grouse *Lyrurus tetrix* and red grouse *Lagopus lagopus scoticus*. Deaths due to collision with deer fencing have been investigated at a number of sites and are thought to have increased since the introduction of weld-mesh-type fencing materials. For capercaillie, these fences are considered to be a major source of mortality (Moss 1987; Catt et al. in press). A collaborative study involving the RSPB, SNH, the Forestry Commission and ITE is currently examining the problem on a wider geographical scale and will be considering possible solutions.

Other concerns which have been expressed in relation to deer fencing include aesthetic impact, restrictions of access and damage to sensitive habitats associated with fence erection and maintenance (Watson 1993).

Consequences of traditional estate management

Central to the philosophy of traditional estate management is the maintenance of large stag numbers for sporting purposes. This emphasis on stags may also reflect the fact that estate capital values are based on the number of stags shot.

High hind numbers on many estates have also been encouraged, partly by default (the value of hinds as a sporting resource is limited to c. £50, compared with c. £250 for stags), and partly as a consequence of the belief that high hind numbers are necessary to attract or produce stags. This latter belief is misguided since there is evidence to suggest that, due to competition for food, stags are disadvantaged by high hind numbers (Clutton-Brock & Albon 1989).

As a consequence of traditional estate management, hinds have been culled below the rate of recruitment in many areas. In 1986 it was estimated that more than 75% of the RDC counting blocks were culling hinds below the rate of recruitment (Clutton-Brock & Albon 1989). This under-culling has contributed to the increasing, and female-biased, red deer population. We recognise, however, the considerable efforts made by some estates in recent years to address the problem of excessive hind numbers.

Traditional estate management has, therefore, contributed in a profound way to the conflicts of interests associated with red deer populations in Scotland. Perversely, traditional estate management has also been instrumental in eroding the very resource it has been attempting to encourage, ie. stags of trophy quality.

The contemporary red deer problem reflects a failure on the part of both estate managers and the scientific community. The latter has failed to communicate effectively the results of red deer research to land-owners, factors and stalkers. For their part, some people involved in estate management have clung to tradition, however misguided.

Under-culling of hinds has contributed to the increasing and female-biased red deer population.

ESTATE MANAGEMENT : RED GROUSE

In north-east Scotland, where heather moorland is traditionally managed for red grouse, declining grouse bags have been attributed to over-grazing by red deer and sheep and the associated loss of heather habitat (Watson 1989). In this and in other aspects of the grouse/red deer relationship there is an abundance of anecdote, but very few hard data.

Where red deer densities are sufficiently high to cause a loss of heather and blaeberry *Vaccinium myrtillus*, it has been speculated that invertebrate abundance may decline, causing a shortage of food for grouse chicks. The habit of leaving unburied grallochs has been suggested as the cause of increased predator populations, especially foxes, and thus of increased grouse predation. Deer are also widely believed to eat grouse eggs, though this is highly unlikely other than in isolated cases. Although scientific evidence is lacking, deer have in the past been linked with the spread of tick-borne louping ill in grouse populations, and in the 1930s a large cull was undertaken in lower Deeside in response to a perceived red grouse tick problem (Staines et al. 1992).

In order to assess the extent to which red deer and red grouse management conflict there is very clearly a need for research. The extent to which grouse and deer could be cropped in a complementary manner from the same area of ground is worthy of further investigation. That which is currently perceived as a problem may, in fact, be an opportunity for effective resource management.

The extent to which grouse and deer could be cropped in a complementary manner from the same area of ground is worthy of further investigation.

Conflicts between people using the hills for recreation and those trying to stalk or cull deer are increasing.

ACCESS AND RECREATION

Conflicts between people using the hills for recreation and those trying to stalk or cull deer are increasing. Staines & Scott (1992) reviewed the issues concerned with disturbance by recreational activities to red deer, and the implications for management. They found no evidence that red deer populations were adversely affected by increased disturbance, there being no apparent difference in deer performance between heavily and lightly used areas. However, they recognised that welfare was an important consideration and that any stress, from shooting as well as from other recreations, at certain times of year, should be minimised if at all possible. They concluded that, so far, there is no hard evidence that culls are not being achieved due to disturbance from visitors. Nevertheless, the authors recognised that the main concern is possible disruption to stag stalking, but that the extent and economic significance of this remain unclear. Furthermore, they acknowledged that stalkers could feel frustrated by the disturbance and disruption which can arise from visitor pressure.

Access to the open hill during the shooting season is becoming a keen issue for hill walkers and estate managers alike. Given the importance we place on improvements in informal access, SNH is always seeking ways to encourage a more amicable approach to reconciling management needs in Highland estates with responsible public access to open land. To demonstrate possible ways forward, SNH has agreed to grant-aid the provision of deer-management access signs in selected localities. We see the signs as encouraging walkers and climbers to take a more responsible attitude and to try to understand better the management needs of the estates. We also see the signs as a way of encouraging sporting estates to be more welcoming and that user-friendly signs might persuade other landowners to remove any signs which are unhelpful or provocative. SNH is looking forward to a positive outcome on this issue and we are encouraging the other parties - owners/managers and users - to enter the discussion with the same approach. SNH is preparing a policy and action programme on Access in Scotland, to be published later this year. This addresses the above issues in the wider context of access to the countryside as a whole.

**FUTURE RED DEER
POPULATIONS**

The more or less discrete sub-populations of red deer
which occur in Scotland should be the basic units of
management. Not only is this biologically realistic, but
these sub-populations also tend to correspond to Deer
Management Group areas. Like the sub-populations of
red deer, these groups transcend individual ownership
boundaries and therefore provide a potentially useful
framework for deer management.

The numbers of deer which it is desirable to have in each
sub-population will depend on management objectives.
Where the production of mature stags with trophy heads
is the prime objective, it will be necessary to maintain
hinds at a relatively low level, in order to reduce feeding
competition. In this case, sex ratios of 1 : 1 are
appropriate. In contrast, maximisation of venison production
requires hind-biased sex ratios, with maximum yield usually being
achieved at population densities just high enough to depress the
growth of individual animals (Mitchell et al. 1977; Red Deer
Commission 1981; Clutton-Brock & Albon 1989). These objectives
must be set in the context of habitat considerations.

*The numbers of deer which it is desirable
to have in each sub-population will
depend on management objectives.*

Where the objective of management is to regenerate native
woodland, deer numbers may have to be reduced considerably. As
woodland habitat becomes established, these reductions in density
are likely to be offset in the longer term by improved animal
condition and productivity (Mitchell et al. 1981; Ratcliffe 1987b).

In other situations, priority may be given to the maintenance of open
plant communities and associated animal species by retaining
relatively high deer densities with reduced growth and fecundity
and higher mortality rates. The latter may benefit carrion-
dependent species such as golden eagles and ravens. Many of these
open plant communities, such as heather moorland, blanket bog and
montane heaths, are of international importance (Francis et al. 1991)
and are listed under the EC Habitats Directive.

The movement of deer into areas of low density created by heavy culling is a common concern. Evidence for the existence of this 'vacuum effect' is however equivocal and there is a need for specific research.

CONCERNS

Many concerns have been expressed over the potential impact of SNH policies with respect to the reduction of red deer numbers in Scotland (eg. Pearson 1991; Wigan 1991). In the following section we appraise these concerns in the light of available evidence. We acknowledge that in some cases these concerns need to be addressed by further research and demonstration.

Loss of revenue due to the 'vacuum effect'

The movement of deer into areas of low density created by heavy culling, and the subsequent loss of potential revenue for adjacent estates, are a common concern. This 'vacuum effect' is a controversial issue and, although no specific research has been undertaken, we can appraise the evidence from existing studies of deer movements and social behaviour.

The strong hefting of red and other related deer, particularly females, is well known (eg Lowe 1966; Craighead et al. 1973; Franklin et al. 1975; Clutton-Brock & Albon 1989).

Evidence from the Red Deer Commission's marking programme in the West Grampians showed that only 10% of hinds were shot more than 8km from their birth area, compared with over 40% of stags (RDC Annual Reports 1983-85).

Long-term studies of red deer on Rum, in which the population on one part of the island was allowed to increase 2.5-3 times its original figure, showed that hinds were strongly hefted to their home ranges and that there was no marked emigration despite the big increase in density. Young stags, however, were affected, with more moving out and fewer immigrating into the area.

At Glen Dye deer numbers were reduced by shooting from c.10/100 ha to 3.4/100 ha over 7 years. Evidence from regular counts and from marked animals suggested that there was no great influx of deer from adjacent areas (Staines 1977, 1978).

Caution is required, however, in the interpretation of both the Rum and Glen Dye studies. On Rum the study area was surrounded by glens with reasonably high densities of deer. Would emigration have taken place if the deer there were at low densities? At Glen Dye, low deer densities surrounded the estate. Would there have been immigration if there had been high deer numbers on neighbouring ground?

At Inshriach and Creag Meagaidh, following heavy culling, there has been no evidence of significant deer movements into these areas following heavy culling.

Any evidence for the existence of a 'vacuum effect' is, therefore, equivocal. There is a need for specific research to examine this issue more closely. Even so, any vacuum effects should not cause unnecessary alarm, because neighbouring estates, by culling hard on their own boundaries, would effectively create buffer zones preventing mass movements out of their land.

Loss of heather moorland

Concern has been expressed at the potential loss of open habitat associated with reductions in deer numbers and with the regeneration of native woodland in the uplands. Heather moorland managed for grouse is a particular focus for concern. The amount of new woodland, however, will be small compared with the areas of open ground remaining. By prioritising different areas in an objective manner it will be possible to quantify the scale of any changes as the basis for dialogue and for an integrated approach to land management.

Loss of revenue to grouse moors due to replacement of moorland by woodland could be compensated for, at least in part, by improved management of the remaining open ground leading to higher grouse densities. In addition, regenerating native woodland, with associated populations of black grouse, capercaillie and red deer, would provide new opportunities for game management.

While the restoration of native woodland is fundamental, we also recognise the importance of maintaining the open habitats below the tree line such as heather moorland and boglands which characterise the wilder uplands of Scotland.

Loss of employment

Reductions in the red deer population need not lead to losses of traditional employment on estates. Initial reductions in deer numbers will require enhanced culling rates and thus create more employment. Where populations of red deer have been reduced, culling effort will need to be maintained, and with lower densities of deer this will be more difficult. Demand for the skills of the stalker are therefore unlikely to decline. As we move towards integrated red deer management it is possible to envisage a skills shortage and that opportunities for stalkers with a sound training in deer and range management will increase.

Capital values & loss of stalking

The capital value attributed to shootable stags has increased dramatically in recent years from £5,000-£8,000 in 1985 to £20,000-£40,000 in 1990 (Callander & MacKenzie 1991), although by 1993 this had declined to £10,000-£20,000 reflecting both the surplus of sporting estates on the market and the economic recession (information supplied by Smiths Gore, Edinburgh). Fears have been expressed that reductions in red deer populations could seriously erode the capital values of estates and additionally result in a loss of stag stalking. However, many estates could maintain or even enhance their current levels of stag stalking with fewer deer on the ground. For example, Clutton-Brock & Albon (1992) have shown that where females are lightly culled and predominate in the adult population, managers should be able to increase both the number and quality of mature males taken each year by raising the culling rate of females; this reflects the fact that high hind densities are associated with a deterioration in aspects of stag body performance, increased stag mortality and stag emigration.

In addition there are other reasons why a loss of stag stalking is unlikely. Stalking (as opposed to culling) is related to the number of beats, stalkers and days available, rather than the total population size. For example, in three estates in the central Cairngorms, the stag cull is the same as it was in 1967; yet the deer stock has doubled. The same stalking could be achieved, therefore, with half, if not less than half, of the current population.

Deer performance

In wild red deer, growth (including antler weight and size) and reproductive success decline with increasing population density. This relationship is well established (Mitchell et al. 1977; Staines 1970, 1978; Albon et al. 1983; Clutton-Brock & Albon 1989, 1992) . Because of this density dependence, individual deer on Highland deer forests perform below their capacity. As a consequence, similar yields of venison or numbers of stags could be achieved with lower deer densities **(Figure 8)**. There are no grounds for the view that deer performance will decline with reductions in the population.

FIGURE 8. Changes in the potential yield of red deer in relation to population density. The general form of the graph will be the same whether the objective of management is to maximise the number of hinds or stags which can be culled or venison production. The arrow indicates the maximum sustainable yield, ie the maximum number of animals which can be culled or maximum venison yield which can be achieved without reducing the population. The overall shape of the graph reflects the influence of density dependence on reproductive output and mortality. (Adapted from Clutton-Brock & Albon 1989)

Point of maximum sustainable yield

Potential yield

Population Density

PART II : POLICIES

Introduction

Red deer management is insufficiently integrated with other land-uses and our broader regard for the natural heritage in the uplands. We seek to change the sectoral approach to the management of such an important natural resource. To this end, this policy paper sets out what SNH intends to do to promote and attain a more sustainable and integrated approach to the management of red deer and their habitats. SNH's stance is highlighted in bold type in the remainder of this section. We are still considering a detailed programme of action, but we believe that the time is right for debate between the various interests on the overall policies required and the actions needed on the ground to deliver them. As stated in the Preface, SNH's role is substantially advisory, whereas the role of RDC is statutory and the role of owners and managers on their own, and through Deer Management Groups, is central.

The red deer resource

Red deer are our largest native herbivores and have been present in Scotland for at least 11,000 years. They are clearly an important part of our natural heritage, with deer forest forming a distinctive and major habitat.

Current numbers of red deer are so high that important elements of the natural heritage are being damaged and others threatened, in some areas.

SNH seeks to work with statutory and voluntary interests to promote sustainable management of red deer and their habitats.

Population reduction

Current numbers of red deer are so high that important elements of the natural heritage are being damaged, and others threatened, in some areas. There are similar concerns regarding forestry and agriculture. The optimum number of deer for a given area will depend upon specific management objectives and priorities. For instance, acceptable densities for the regeneration of native woodlands and other sensitive habitats will be lower than those required to optimise venison production.

SNH accepts and supports the Red Deer Commission's proposal to reduce the overall red deer population by 100,000 animals as a first step towards integrated management.

The regeneration of native woodland could generate substantial benefits for game managers in the long term. In addition to larger, more productive deer, populations of black grouse and capercaillie should also increase.

SNH regards it as essential for deer range managers, with input from RDC in particular and with advice from other interests including SNH, to define optimum populations at the local level. These should be set within the framework of a Management Plan which, it is hoped, will be developed by each Deer Management Group in Scotland.

Management Plans

Many of the problems associated with red deer in Scotland arise from a sectoral approach to their management. Red deer have been managed in isolation from other human activities and from environmental considerations.

As a matter of urgency, an integrated approach to red deer management is required throughout their range. The Red Deer Commission and the Deer Management Groups should be in the lead to achieve this. SNH is committed to working with them as advisors on natural heritage matters.

SNH will provide advice on the definition of management objectives for the natural heritage at the local level.

Habitat change : relative roles of sheep & deer

Red deer influence vegetation change in the uplands. An evaluation of their impact, however, is confounded by the presence of c.2 million sheep over a shared range. While declines in the area of heather moorland, for example, have occurred, the specific role of red deer remains to be quantified. Greater understanding of the effects of given numbers of deer compared with sheep on vegetation change is needed. Existing knowledge in this respect is inadequate, and based either on experimental plots or small areas not representative of the uplands as a whole. There is a need for whole-range studies, both of deer alone, and with sheep or cattle. These will vastly improve understanding of habitat change, and will enhance the quality of SNH's environmental input to Management Plans.

Adverse changes in the upland environment are not due solely to red deer. The contribution of upland sheep farming must also be considered. There is an urgent need to identify the relationships between upland herbivores and their habitat, so that local Management Plans can be refined accordingly. SNH will work with other interests in promoting the commissioning of whole-range grazing studies.

SNH will ensure that the results of previous work, published and unpublished, on the interactions between grazing animals in the uplands and their effect on habitats, are translated into practical advice and guidance for the improved management of the deer range. Priorities and plans for new research should also be identified.

SNH will instigate discussions with SOAFD on potential mechanisms for overcoming the detrimental effects of heavy grazing by domestic stock and associated poor management, such as haphazard muirburn, without damaging the financial viability of the hill farming sector.

Woodland regeneration

Native woodland is one of the few habitats for which there is good evidence that red deer alone are preventing regeneration. Their extent and diversity have been suppressed largely by grazing and browsing.

Most of the remaining fragments are approaching the end of their productive lives. Their regeneration should be promoted where it does not conflict with the management of other open habitats which we also value. Where appropriate, priority should be given to establishing areas of continuous woodland ranging from lower ground up to tree-line scrub. This may come about through the outward expansion of woodland and scrub from inaccessible gorges, cliffs and corries or, on a grander scale, across entire hillsides. Large reductions in the red deer population will be required locally to promote this regeneration. Nevertheless, once woodland is established, red deer can find their proper place as an integral and essential part of the uplands and their woodland ecosystems. The regeneration of this woodland could generate substantial benefits for game managers in the long term. Woodland red deer will develop into larger, more productive animals; populations of black grouse and capercaillie should increase.

SNH will identify those woodlands of high priority which, as a result of grazing and browsing by deer, are not regenerating. This task must be undertaken in conjunction with the RDC and Deer Management Groups.

Conventional management

Conventional management of red deer for stalking has, in part, contributed to the present day problems associated with red deer. This is dominated by traditions which extend back to the mid-19th century, when high numbers of hinds were deemed necessary to retain stags. This has been a significant factor in the contemporary population increase. However, it has been counter-productive from the estate manager's point of view. Open hill populations of red deer are generally under-performing in terms of the growth, survival and reproductive potential of individuals. This is due to the operation of density-dependent factors. In addition, stags are disadvantaged due to competition with hinds, at high densities, over food. We recognise the significant effort made by deer managers and their stalkers to reduce hind populations over the past three years.

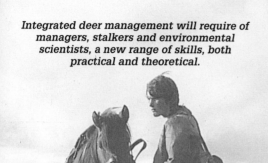

Integrated deer management will require of managers, stalkers and environmental scientists, a new range of skills, both practical and theoretical.

We consider that whether the objective of management is to optimise the production of venison, or trophy stags, or both, reductions in population density, particularly of hinds, will be beneficial.

Revision of Red Deer Management Handbook

The existing Red Deer Management Handbook, produced by the Red Deer Commission (HMSO 1981), should be updated and revised to include reference to natural heritage considerations and the results of recent research.

SNH would like to assist the Red Deer Commission in the revision of the Red Deer Management Handbook.

Demonstration projects

Owners of upland estates and their managers pay more heed to demonstrations of good management than to scientific treatises. A major programme of demonstrations will show, by example, the benefits of integrated deer management for sustaining the interests of deer estates as well as those of the natural heritage. Such demonstrations should not be confined to statutory conservation sites.

SNH advocates the establishment of a major programme of demonstrations throughout the deer range in Scotland. This would involve all the key interests, but with the Deer Management Groups in the lead. The RDC should play a key role, with SNH an active participant on natural heritage issues. For its part, SNH would like to see demonstrations which would show the following:

- **the benefits of reduced population density, particularly hinds,to the natural heritage and to estate economics;**

- **the potential for integrating red deer management, in economic and natural heritage terms, with sheep, cattle, game birds, forestry and recreation;**

- **the use of simple computer models to guide decision-making in setting cull levels, including the minimum population required to sustain given yields of stags. These models are currently being developed for the Red Deer Commission under contract;**

- **the costs and benefits of woodland regeneration;**

- **simple but meaningful methods of deer population assessment and monitoring of habitat condition;**

- the role of supplementary feeding as a management tool for controlling deer movements and impacts;

- whether or not burning is necessary on deer forest; and good burning practice;

- good culling and carcase extraction practices.

Education and training

Integrated deer management will require of managers, stalkers and environmental scientists, including SNH staff, a new range of skills, both practical and theoretical. They will need an up-to-date knowledge of deer ecology and of simple techniques for monitoring habitat, deer condition and deer productivity. They will need to be familiar with record-keeping, analysis and interpretation. Existing opportunities for formal education in these areas are limited.

SNH will work with training course providers to ensure that they incorporate natural heritage considerations in the curriculum for deer management.

SNH will collaborate with educational institutions to produce teaching material concerning management of the natural heritage in the deer range, in partnership with the Red Deer Commission and the Forestry Commission.

SNH sees the need for rationalisation and better targeting of red deer management courses for stalkers, factors and land owners. This is best based on the award-winning Forestry Commission model. SNH seeks jointly to pursue this in collaboration with the Red Deer Commission, the Forestry Commission, the Institute of Terrestrial Ecology and the Game Conservancy, among others. SNH will be prepared to consider joint funding of courses.

Standardised recording of the cull

Data collection in the past has been haphazard and inconsistent. The establishment of a standardised recording system for documenting information on every deer culled is central to good deer management. It enables aspects of deer performance to be monitored, providing the basis for informed management decisions.

SNH will support the Red Deer Commission in its desire to devise and implement a standardised system for documenting the annual cull. This should include information on age, sex, weight, health and reproductive status of every deer culled.

Accurate assessment of the red deer population, in terms of local numbers and population structure is a prerequisite of substainable resource management.

Role of Deer Management Groups

Red deer occur in more or less discrete sub-populations. These cross individual ownership boundaries, and management structures should reflect this distribution. Sub-populations are the basic units of management and, as such, tend to coincide with Deer Management Group areas.

SNH believes that Deer Management Groups provide the key to integrated management of red deer and their habitat.

Although these voluntary groups currently have an important role, and we recognise the significant progress made, their full potential has yet to be realised. For example, non-membership by estates which adopt outmoded deer management practices can inhibit progress. On the other hand, some groups are successfully moving towards integrated deer management. These achievements should be recognised.

Given the pivotal role of Deer Management Groups, and the breadth of action required, we propose to assist these Groups in their endeavours, in consultation with the RDC. We recommend the provision of funding, tied to an agreed Management Plan which will enhance the natural heritage.

SNH will seek to ensure that it is represented on every Deer Management Group.

SNH strongly supports the Red Deer Commission in its desire to see every Deer Management Group adopt a Management Plan for the red deer and their habitat within the Group's domain. SNH recognises that this is a considerable undertaking for DMGs, for the RDC and for itself, and therefore will discuss with the Association and the Commission how to take this forward.

SNH wishes to consider jointly with the RDC and the Association of Deer Management Groups the means whereby culling levels can be increased in order to enhance the benefit to the natural heritage and the red deer stocks. SNH established a demonstration project for 1993/94 with the East Grampian Deer Management Group; the key element in this experiment was an undertaking to underwrite the net costs of culling required to reduce red deer populations towards levels compatible with the enhancement of the natural heritage.

While recognising the strengths and achievements of DMGs, the importance of developing an integrated approach to the management of red deer and their range is such that the voluntary role of DMGs should be under continual review by the RDC to examine both their success and the possibility of their establishment under statute. SNH is happy to make a positive input to this ongoing review.

Deer counts

Accurate assessment of the red deer population, in terms of local numbers and population structure, is a prerequisite of sustainable resource management. This forms the basis for monitoring the response of the population to culling, and provides a measure of the extent to which management objectives are being achieved. Deer Management Groups are well placed to define the size and structure of the sub-populations which they cover, and some DMGs already organise regular counts.

SNH recognises the need for a co-ordinated approach to training for deer managers and welcomes the Red Deer Commission's recent initiative in this respect. We shall assist the Red Deer Commission in its endeavours to develop co-ordinated training through the provision of advice on aspects of the natural heritage.

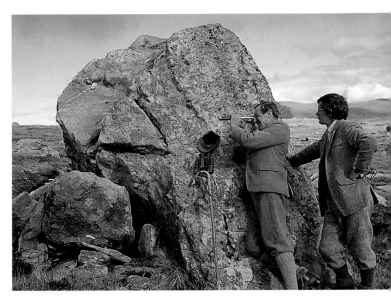

SNH recognises the need for a co-ordinated approach to training for deer managers.

SNH supports the Red Deer Commission in its continuing efforts to audit deer counts made by Deer Management Groups.

SNH will continue to collaborate with the Red Deer Commission to develop novel supplementary counting techniques, such as thermal imaging.

Legislation

Contemporary management of red deer populations is undertaken in the context of the Deer (Scotland) Act 1959. Originally drafted with a view to providing a legislative framework for dealing with problems associated with agriculture, forestry and poaching, the legislation is now in urgent need of revision. With this in mind, Government has undertaken wide consultation.

SNH has pressed for new legislation which acknowledges unequivocally that management of red deer populations for the protection and enhancement of the natural heritage is a legitimate and necessary provision, equal in weight, and not unrelated to, the need to protect agricultural and forestry interests.

A change in emphasis from conservation and control to furthering integrated sustainable management of wild red deer should be central to any new legislation, with a requirement to consider all appropriate economic, environmental and social factors.

The use of all-terrain vehicles for carcase extraction is increasing. ATVs can adversely affect natural heritage interests by destroying vegetation cover and increasing the potential for soil erosion.

Existing legislation makes provision for the Red Deer Commission, with the approval of the Secretary of State, to establish Panels for the purposes of addressing local issues relating to red deer, agriculture and forestry. SNH supports the RDC in its desire to increase both the representation and scope of these Panels to include the natural heritage interest.

SNH should be identified in any new legislation as the Red Deer Commission's (or its successor's) statutory adviser on natural heritage issues.

Under existing legislation, the Red Deer Commission can only authorise shooting outwith close seasons for the purpose of preventing serious damage to agriculture and forestry. Ordinarily, stags can be shot during the period 1 July-20 October; hinds can be shot from 21 October-15 February. The existing close seasons are embodied in primary legislation and cannot therefore be varied except by Act of Parliament.

SNH considers that revised legislation should make provision for the Red Deer Commission to authorise shooting out of season for the purpose of protecting the natural heritage. Provision should also be made for the Secretary of State to vary close seasons by Order.

Fencing

Although fencing has been extensively used to contain red deer or exclude them from vulnerable areas, there are a number of associated problems. These include disruption of range-use by deer, intensification of grazing outwith fenced areas, adverse impacts on capercaillie and black grouse populations, visual impact on the landscape, restriction of access and expense. SNH wants to see the restoration of habitats in the presence of red deer, albeit at lower densities, and is of the opinion that this will promote the development of vegetation of a more natural character.

In deer control schemes, culling and fencing should be seen not as opposing alternatives but as complementary management tools, to be used as circumstances require.

We recognise that in some situations, such as the regeneration of native woodland or of open-hill habitats, the scale of culling required may be such that fencing is the pragmatic management option. Such fencing should be undertaken on a rotational basis. For example, where woodland regeneration is required, this could be achieved over a number of years by fencing a certain percentage of ground each year. Once the earliest protected woodlands are safe from browsing, fences could be removed, allowing deer access to the woodland. Similar areas of open ground could then be fenced.

SNH is prepared, in consultation with the RDC, to give financial support for fencing in priority areas where there are likely to be relatively rapid natural heritage benefits. In such circumstances, part of the conditions for financial assistance will be to ensure that densities of deer outwith enclosed areas are reduced to compensate for loss of habitat and to protect the natural heritage.

In forest plantations the maintenance of boundary fences can be critical for the control of deer. Where fencing is neglected or inadequately maintained the difficulty of culling deer on adjacent open-hill may be increased.

SNH wants to see the restoration of habitats in the presence of red deer, albeit at lower densities.

SNH will encourage Forest Enterprise and other landowners to maintain the fences around plantations, where appropriate, in order to aid deer population control.

Culling methods

SNH welcomes the increasing culling effort being made by many estates, resulting in the largest cull of hinds and followers since records began (c.43,500 in 1992/93). In order to achieve further reductions in the red deer population, these culling rates, particularly of hinds, will have to be maintained and in some instances increased.

SNH believes that in achieving reductions in the red deer population, managers should not be constrained by the traditions of stalking, but should consider and investigate alternative methods of deer numbers reduction such as live capture.

SNH will ensure that all culling methods employed on land under its jurisdiction are humane.

Carcase extraction

Traditionally, carcases have been removed from the hill by pony. However, partly in response to declining levels of permanent employment on estates, the use of all-terrain vehicles (ATVs) for both carcase extraction and the transport of fee-paying stalkers is increasing. As culling levels rise and restrictions on the time between culling and lardering are implemented through statutory (EC Wild Game Meat Directive) or private sector agreements (Safeways venison marketing initiative), the use of these vehicles is likely to increase further. ATVs can adversely affect natural heritage interests by destroying vegetation cover and increasing

the potential for soil erosion. While the traditional method of carcase extraction by pony is compatible with the natural heritage and is therefore preferred, we recognise that this method in isolation may limit the success of attempts to reduce the red deer population.

SNH recommends that carcases should be extracted by environmentally sensitive means. SNH will produce a Code of Guidance on the use of all-terrain vehicles.

Supplementary feeding

The role of supplementary feeding is ambiguous in terms of its effects on red deer population dynamics, emigration and immigration rates, habitat-use and impacts.

SNH recognises the potential importance of supplementary feeding as a management tool. We shall encourage research to investigate the use of supplementary feeding as a means of diverting grazing pressure from sensitive parts of the winter range.

The provision of supplementary food for hinds is likely to increase calving rates and thus contribute to further population increases. However, the provision of local fertilised areas of grassland within wintering grounds may facilitate efficient culling of hinds within the existing open season.

SNH considers that there should be a presumption against supplementary feeding of hinds, except where this aids efficient and humane culling.

Hybridisation

Hybridisation with introduced sika deer poses a significant threat to the genetic integrity of native red deer. Under the Deer (Scotland) Act 1959, both sika and sika/red hybrids are protected by close seasons.

SNH urges the withdrawal of close seasons for sika and sika/red hybrids in specific areas where natural heritage interests are compromised.

Sika deer are primarily woodland dwellers and their eradication is extremely difficult, if not impossible, using current culling methods. Their expanding range, increasing density and the difficulty of their control are due mainly to the spread and structure of plantation forestry. The short rotation length of many plantations is associated with a high proportion of pre canopy-closure stages which hold high densities of sika, red and roe deer. Forest design, such as the provision of open areas, is essential to aid culling;

longer rotation lengths, where practical, would also assist control by reducing the amount of preferred habitat. However, current opinion is that sika deer are uncontrollable in forestry plantations and that continued hybridisation seems inevitable in some areas.

SNH considers that the problem of sika deer deserves separate and urgent consideration and supports the inter-agency Working Group recently established to address it. This Group comprises representatives from Scottish Natural Heritage, the Red Deer Commission, the Forestry Commission and the Institute of Terrestrial Ecology.

SNH, with the RDC, will give further consideration to the identification of sika and hybrid-free Refuge Areas for red deer where sika could be excluded by culling and habitat management.

Funding

It is widely recognised that the work of the RDC has been hindered not only by the restraints in statute but also by the low level of resources it has available to devote to red deer management. Given the importance that SNH, as well as many other organisations, place on improved red deer management, and given also our view that the powers of RDC should be redefined as stated earlier, we advocate that the Commission be given enhanced funding.

SNH welcomes the additional funding given to the Red Deer Commission for the year 1994-95 and hopes that when new legislation is enacted, resources commensurate with fulfilling its wider role will be provided. Any new legislation should make provision for the Red Deer Commission to give grant aid to other bodies for the purpose of achieving sustainable deer management.

SNH devotes a considerable amount of resources to red deer and red deer range management issues at present. It will be undertaking a review of priorities and resources to be devoted to these issues in the future.

SNH will encourage research to investigate the use of supplementary feeding as a means of diverting grazing pressure from sensitive parts of the winter range.

SNH proposes that exemptions from Inheritance Tax for land of national scenic importance or special scientific interest should only be granted on condition that a properly approved Red Deer Management Plan is available.

SNH can envisage situations in which the integrated management of the red deer population in a given area could improve the natural heritage interests to a level where Inheritance Tax exemption would be appropriate.

Adverse changes in the upland environment are not due solely to red deer. The contribution of upland sheep farming must also be considered.

Accreditation scheme

Integrated and sustainable deer management should be recognised as a highly prestigious and desirable part of land-management.

SNH recommends that the Red Deer Commission, Association of Deer Management Groups and venison dealers consider promoting an accreditation scheme. SNH would wish to be involved in such a scheme if it had clear environmental criteria. It would be appropriate for such a scheme to have an award for good practice.

National Nature Reserves

On its owned NNRs SNH will demonstrate, by example, good deer management practice. On other Reserves SNH will, as part of a wide ranging review of Reserves, consider how improvements in deer management practice can be brought about.

Grazing pressures in the uplands

The policies and action points above are considered vital if we are to achieve fully integrated red deer management across Scotland. When implemented, the first steps will have been taken towards the restoration and enhancement of our natural heritage. However, we are concerned that hill sheep farming is also having an adverse impact in parts of the uplands. We acknowledge that Environmentally Sensitive Area designations and the Heather Extensification Scheme are positive initiatives in this respect. Nevertheless, we remain concerned that unless the problems of heavy grazing by sheep and associated management are addressed more widely, efforts to resolve the conflicts posed by red deer in relation to the natural heritage will be undermined.

SNH will pursue further discussions with SOAFD and SOEnD on broad grazing-related problems in the uplands.

SUMMARY

The red deer resource

SNH seeks to work with statutory and voluntary interests to promote sustainable management of red deer and their habitats. (p45)

Population reduction

SNH accepts and supports the Red Deer Commission's proposal to reduce the overall red deer population by 100,000 animals as a first step towards integrated management. (p45)

SNH regards it essential for deer range managers, with input from the RDC in particular and with advice from other interests including SNH, to define optimum populations at the local level. These should be set within the framework of a Management Plan which, it is hoped, will be developed by each Deer Management Group in Scotland. (p46)

Management Plans

As a matter of urgency, an integrated approach to red deer management is required throughout their range. The Red Deer Commission and the Deer Management Groups should be in the lead to achieve this. SNH is committed to working with them as advisors on natural heritage matters. (p46)

SNH will provide advice on the definition of management objectives for the natural heritage at the local level. (p46)

Habitat change : relative roles of deer & sheep

Adverse changes in the upland environment are not due solely to red deer. The contribution of upland sheep farming must also be considered. There is an urgent need to identify the relationships between upland herbivores and their habitat, so that local Management Plans can be refined accordingly. SNH will work with other interests in promoting the commissioning of whole-range grazing studies. (p46)

SNH will ensure that the results of previous work, published and unpublished, on the interactions between grazing animals in the uplands and their effect on habitats, are translated into practical advice and guidance for the improved management of the deer range. Priorities and plans for new research should also be identified. (p46)

SNH will instigate discussions with SOAFD on potential mechanisms for overcoming the detrimental effects of heavy

SNH will pursue further discussions with SOAFD and SOEnD on broad grazing-related problems in the uplands.

grazing by domestic stock and associated poor management, such as haphazard muirburn, without damaging the financial viability of the hill farming sector. (p47)

Woodland regeneration

SNH will identify those woodlands of high priority which, as a result of grazing and browsing by deer, are not regenerating. This task must be undertaken in conjunction with the RDC and Deer Management Groups. (p47)

Conventional management

We consider that whether the objective of management is to optimise the production of venison or trophy stags, or both, reductions in population density, particularly of hinds, will be beneficial. (p48)

Red deer management handbook

SNH would like to assist the Red Deer Commission in the revision of the Red Deer Management Handbook. (p48)

Demonstration projects

SNH advocates the establishment of a major programme of demonstrations throughout the deer range in Scotland. This would involve all the key interests, but with the Deer Management Groups in the lead. The RDC should play a key role, with SNH an active participant on natural heritage issues. SNH would like to see several issues addressed in these demonstrations. (p48)

Education & training

SNH will work with training course providers to ensure that they incorporate natural heritage considerations in the curriculum for deer management. (p49)

SNH will collaborate with educational institutions to produce teaching material concerning management of the natural heritage in the deer range, in partnership with the Red Deer Commission and the Forestry Commission. (p49)

SNH sees the need for rationalisation and better targeting of red deer management courses for stalkers, factors and land owners. This is best based on the award-winning Forestry Commission model. SNH seeks jointly to pursue this in collaboration with the Red Deer Commission, the Forestry Commission, the Institute of Terrestrial Ecology and the Game Conservancy, among others. SNH will be prepared to consider joint funding of courses. (p49)

Standardised recording

SNH will support the Red Deer Commission in its desire to devise and implement a standardised system for documenting the annual cull. This should include information on age, sex, weight, health and reproductive status of every deer culled. (p49)

Role of Deer Management Groups

SNH believes that Deer Management Groups provide the key to integrated management of red deer and their habitat. (p50)

SNH will seek to ensure that it is represented on every Deer Management Group. (p50)

SNH strongly supports the Red Deer Commission in its desire to see every Deer Management Group adopt a Management Plan for the red deer and their habitat within the Group's domain. SNH recognises that this is a considerable undertaking for DMGs, for the RDC and for itself, and therefore will discuss with the Association and the Commission how to take this forward. (p50)

SNH wishes to consider jointly with the Red Deer Commission and the Association of Deer Management Groups the means whereby culling levels can be increased in order to enhance the benefit to the natural heritage and the red deer stocks. SNH established a demonstration project for 1993/94 with the East Grampian Deer Management Group; the key element in this experiment was an undertaking to underwrite the net costs of culling required to reduce red deer populations towards levels compatible with the enhancement of the natural heritage. (p50)

While recognising the strengths and achievements of Deer Management Groups, the importance of developing an integrated approach to the management of red deer and their range is such that the voluntary role of DMGs should be under continual review by the Red Deer Commission to examine both their success and the possibility of their establishment under statute. SNH is happy to make a positive input to this ongoing review.(p50)

Deer counts

SNH recognises the need for a co-ordinated approach to training for deer managers and welcomes the Red Deer Commission's recent initiative in this respect. We shall assist the Red Deer Commission in its endeavours to develop co-ordinated training through the provision of advice on aspects of the natural heritage. (p51)

SNH supports the Red Deer Commission in its continuing efforts to audit deer counts made by Deer Management Groups. (p51)

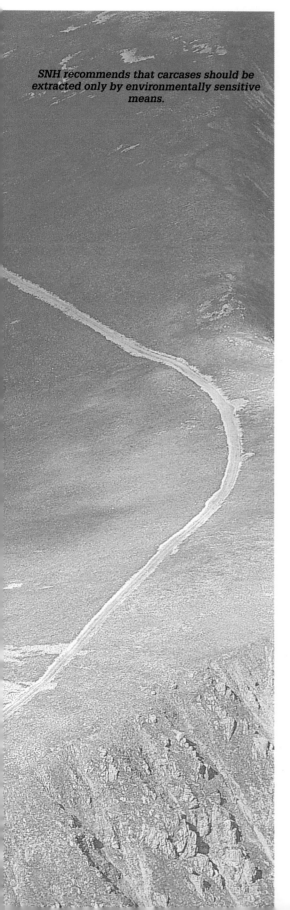

SNH recommends that carcases should be extracted only by environmentally sensitive means.

SNH will continue to collaborate with the Red Deer Commission to develop novel supplementary counting techniques, such as thermal imaging. (p51)

Legislation

SNH has pressed for new legislation which acknowledges unequivocally that management of red deer populations for the protection and enhancement of the natural heritage is a legitimate and necessary provision, equal in weight, and not unrelated to, the need to protect agricultural and forestry interests. (p51)

SNH should be identified in any new legislation as the Red Deer Commission's (or its successor's) statutory adviser on natural heritage issues. (p52)

SNH considers that revised legislation should make provision for the Red Deer Commission to authorise shooting out of season for the purpose of protecting the natural heritage. Provision should also be made for the Secretary of State to vary close seasons by Order. (p52)

Fencing

In deer control schemes, culling and fencing should be seen not as opposing alternatives but as complementary management tools, to be used as circumstances require. (p52)

SNH is prepared, in consultation with the Red Deer Commission, to give financial support for fencing in priority areas where there are likely to be relatively rapid natural heritage benefits. In such circumstances, part of the conditions for financial assistance will be to ensure that densities of deer outwith enclosed areas are reduced to compensate for loss of habitat and to protect the natural heritage. (p53)

SNH will encourage Forest Enterprise and other landowners to maintain the fences around plantations, where appropriate, in order to aid deer population control. (p53)

Culling methods

SNH believes that in achieving reductions in the red deer population, managers should not be constrained by the traditions of stalking, but should consider and investigate alternative methods of deer numbers reduction such as live capture. (p53)

SNH will ensure that all culling methods employed on land under its jurisdiction are humane. (p53)

Carcase extraction

SNH recommends that carcases should be extracted only by environmentally sensitive means. SNH will produce a Code of Guidance on the use of all-terrain vehicles. (p54)

Supplementary feeding

SNH recognises the potential importance of supplementary feeding as a management tool. We shall encourage research to investigate the use of supplementary feeding as a means of diverting grazing pressure from sensitive parts of the winter range. (p54)

SNH considers that there should be a presumption against supplementary feeding of hinds, except where this aids efficient and humane culling. (p54)

Hybridisation

SNH urges the withdrawal of close seasons for sika and sika/red hybrids in specific areas where natural heritage interests are compromised. (p54)

SNH considers that the problem of sika deer deserves separate and urgent consideration, and supports the inter-agency Working Group recently established to address it. SNH, with the RDC, will give further consideration to the identification of sika and hybrid-free Refuge Areas for red deer where sika could be excluded by culling and habitat management. (p55)

Funding

SNH welcomes the additional funding given to the Red Deer Commission for the year 1994-95 and hopes that, when new legislation is enacted, resources commensurate with fulfilling its wider role will be provided. Any new legislation should make provision for the Red Deer Commission to give grant-aid to other bodies for the purpose of achieving sustainable deer management. (p55)

SNH can envisage situations in which the integrated management of the red deer population in a given area could improve the natural heritage interests to a level where Inheritance Tax exemption would be appropriate. (p55)

In deer control schemes, culling and fencing should be seen not as opposing alternatives but as complementary management tools, to be used as circumstances require.

Accreditation scheme

SNH recommends that the Red Deer Commission, Association of Deer Management Groups and venison retailers consider promoting an accreditation scheme. SNH would wish to be involved in such a scheme if it had clear environmental criteria. It would be appropriate for such a scheme to have an award for good practice. (p56)

National Nature Reserves

On its owned NNRs, SNH will demonstrate, by example, good deer management practice. On other Reserves SNH will, as part of a wide ranging review of Reserves, consider how improvements in deer management practice can be brought about. (p56)

Grazing pressures in the uplands

SNH will pursue further discussions with SOAFD and SOEnD on broad grazing-related problems in the uplands. (p56).

On its owned NNRs, SNH will demonstrate, by example, good deer management practice.

REFERENCES

Ahlèn,I. 1965. Studies of the red deer *Cervus elaphus* in Scandinavia 111. Ecological investigations. Viltrevy 3, 177-376.

Albon,S.D. 1983. Ecological aspects of growth, reproduction and mortality in female red deer. PhD Thesis, University of East Anglia.

Albon,S.D., Mitchell,B. & Staines,B.W. 1983. Fertility and body weight in female red deer - a density dependent relationship. J.Anim.Ecol.,52, 969-980.

Allison,M. 1990. Deer management - a view to the 90s. Forestry & British Timber, August.

Arman,P. 1971. Nutritional and physiological studies on captive red deer. In Range Ecology Research. 1st Progress Report, pp.75-78. The Nature Conservancy, Edinburgh.

Baines,D. & Sage,R. 1991. Capercaillie decline and caterpillar abundance in Highland pinewoods. Game Conservancy Review.

Balharry,D. 1993. Factors affecting the distribution and population density of Pine Martens *Martes martes* in Scotland. PhD thesis, University of Aberdeen.

Ball,M.E. 1974. Floristic changes on grasslands and heaths on the Isle of Rhum after a reduction or exclusion of grazing. J.Envir.Mgmnt. 2, 299-318.

Ball,M.E. *in prep*. Long term floristic changes on grazed grasslands and heaths under variable grazing regimes on the Isle of Rum, Scotland. Scottish Natural Heritage, Inverness.

Beddington,J.R. 1975. Economic and ecological analysis of red deer harvesting in Scotland. Journal of Environmental Management, 3, 91-103.

Blaxter,K.L., Kay,R.N.B., Sharman,G.A.M., Cunningham,J.M.M. & Hamilton,W.J. 1974. Farming the red deer. HMSO, Edinburgh.

Brown, L.H. & Watson, A. 1964. The golden eagle in relation to its food supply. Ibis, 106, 78-100.

Cairngorms Working Party Report 1993. Common Sense and Sustainability: a Partnership for the Cairngorms. Report to the Secretary of State for Scotland. HMSO.

Callander,R.F.& MacKenzie,N.M. 1991. The management of wild red deer in Scotland. Rural Forum Scotland.

Cameron,A.G. 1923. The wild red deer of Scotland. Blackwood & Sons, Edinburgh & London.

Catt,D.C., Dugan,D., Green,R.E., Moncrieff,R., Moss,R., Picozzi,N., Summers,R.W. & Tyler,G.A. Collisions against fences by woodland grouse in Scotland. *in press.*

Charles,W.N., McCowan,D. & East,K. 1977. Selection of upland swards by red deer *Cervus elaphus* on Rum, Scotland. Journal of Applied Ecology, 14, 55-64.

Clutton-Brock,T.H. & Albon,S.D. 1989. Red deer in the Highlands. BSP Professional Books, Oxford.

Clutton-Brock, T.H. Price,O.F. Albon, S.D & Jewell, P.A. 1991. Persistent instability and population regulation in Soay sheep. J. Anim. Ecol. 60:593-608.

Clutton-Brock,T.H. & Albon.S.D. 1992. Trial and error in the Highlands. Nature, 358, 11-12.

Colquhoun, I.R. 1971. The grazing ecology of red deer and blackface sheep in Perthshire, Scotland. PhD thesis, University of Edinburgh.

Craighead, J.J. Craighead, F.C. Jnr., Ruff, R.L. & O'Gara, B.W. 1973. Home ranges and activity patterns of non-migratory elk of the Madison Drainage herd as determined by biotelemetry. Wildl.Monogr., 33.

Cramp, S. et al. 1980. The birds of the Western Palearctic. Volume 11. Oxford University Press.

Cummins, R.P. & Miller, G.R. 1982. Damage by red deer *Cervus elaphus* enclosed in planted woodland. Scott.For.36, 1-8.

Darling, F.F. 1937. A herd of red deer. OUP. London.

Darling, F.F. 1955. West Highland Survey. Oxford University Press, London.

Dunnet, S.C. 1974. Attempts at relocation of wintering red deer in south Inverness-shire. MSc thesis. Univ.Aberdeen.

Dunnet, S.C. 1975. Diversionary feeding and red deer. Deer, 3, 447-452.

Francis, J.M., Balharry, R. & Thompson, D.B. 1991. The implications for upland management: a summary paper. In: Deer, Mountains and Man. Ed. H.Rose. British Deer Society and Red Deer Commission.

Franklin, W.L., Mossman, A.S. & Dole, M. 1975. Social organisation and home range of Roosevelt elk. J.Mammal., 56, 102-118.

Fraser of Allander Institute. 1990. The economic impact of sporting shooting in Scotland. Glasgow.

Gill,R. 1990. Monitoring the status of European and North American Cervids. GEMS Information Series No.8, Global Environment Monitoring System. Nairobi: United Nations Environment Programme.

Gordon,I.J. 1989. Vegetation community selection by ungulates on the isle of Rum. II. Vegetation community selection. J.Appl.Ecol.26, 53-64.

Gordon,S. 1925. The Cairngorm Hills of Scotland. Cassell, London.

Gubbins,N. 1992. Sustainability and deer stalking. Scottish Natural Heritage Policy Guidance Paper 4(a).

Harrington,R. 1973. Hybridisation among deer and its implications for conservation. Irish Forestry Journal,30, 64-78.

Harrington,R. 1982. The hybridisation of red deer *Cervus elaphus* and Japanese sika deer *C.nippon*. Transactions of the International Congress of Game Biology, 14, 559-571.

Hewson, R. 1983. The food of wild cats *Felix sylvestris* and red foxes *Vulpes vulpes* in west and north-east Scotland. J.Zool.Lond. 200, 283-289.

Hewson,R. & Kolb,H.H. 1976. Scavenging on sheep carcasses by foxes *Vulpes vulpes* and badgers *Meles meles*. J.Zool.Lond. 180, 496-498.

HMSO. 1954. Report of the Committee on close seasons for deer in Scotland. Edinburgh.

Hobson,P.N, Mann,S.O, Summers, R. & Staines, B.W. 1976. Rumen function in red deer, hill sheep and reindeer in the Scottish Highlands. Proc.R.Soc.Edinb., 75, 181-198.

Holloway,C.W. 1967. The effects of red deer and other animals on naturally regenerated Scots pine. PhD thesis. University of Aberdeen.

Jarvie,E. 1979. The red deer industry: finance and employment 1978-79. Scottish Landowners Federation, Edinburgh.

Lockie,J.D. 1963. Eagles, foxes and their food supply in Wester Ross. Scottish Agriculture. Spring, 186-189.

Lockie,J.D. 1964. The breeding density of the golden eagle and fox in relation to food supply in Wester Ross, Scotland. Scottish Naturalist, 71, 67-77.

Lowe,V.P.W. 1961. A discussion on the history, present status and future conservation of red deer *Cervus elaphus* L. in Scotland. Terre Vie, 1, 9-40.

Lowe,V.P.W. 1966. Observations on the dispersal of red deer on Rum. In: Play, territory and exploration in mammals. Eds. P.A. Jewell & C. Loizon. Academic Press, Lond. 211-228.

Lowe,V.P.W. 1969. Population dynamics of the red deer *Cervus elaphus* L. on Rum. J.Anim.Ecol. 38, 425-457.

Lowe,V.P.W. 1971. Some effects of a change in estate management on a deer population. In: The Scientific Management of Animal and Plant communities for Conservation. (Ed by E.Duffey & A.S.Watt). pp.437-456. Blackwell Scientific Publications, Oxford.

Lowe,V.P.W. & Gardiner,A.S. 1974. A re-examination of the sub-species of red deer *Cervus elaphus* with particular reference to the stocks in Britain. J. Zool. , Lond. 174, 185201.

Lowe,V.P.W. & Gardiner,A.S. 1975. Hybridisation between red deer *Cervus elaphus* and sika deer *Cervus nippon* with particular reference to stocks in N.W.England. J.Zool.,Lond.,177, 553-566.

Marrs,R.H. & Welch,D. 1991. Moorland wilderness: the potential effects of removing domestic livestock, particularly sheep. Institute of Terrestrial Ecology. Report to the Department of Environment.

McLean,C. 1993. Sika deer control: a report on a three-year project in Shin Forest, Sutherland. Internal report, Red Deer Commission.

McVean,D.N. & Lockie,J.D. 1969. Ecology and land use in upland Scotland. Edinburgh University Press, Edinburgh.

Miles,J. 1971. Burning Molinia-dominant vegetation for grazing by red deer. J.Br.Grassland Soc.,26, 247-250.

Mikes, J. 1985. The pedogenic effects of different species and vegetation types and the implications of succession. Journal of Soil Science, 36, 571-584.

Mitchell,B., Staines,B.W., & Welch,D. 1977. Ecology of Red Deer: a research review relevant to their management in Scotland. Natural Environment Research Council, Institute of Terrestrial Ecology.

Mitchell,B., Grant,W. & Cubby,J. 1981. Notes on the performance of red deer *Cervus elaphus* in a woodland habitat. J.Zool.194, 279-284.

Mitchell,B., McCowan,D. & Parish,T. 1986. Performance and population dynamics in relation to management of red deer *Cervus elaphus* at Glenfeshie, Inverness-shire, Scotland. Biological Conservation. 37(3), 237-267.

Mitchell,F.J.G. & Kirby,K.J. 1990. The impact of large herbivores on the conservation of semi-natural woods in the British uplands. Forestry, 63(4), 333-353.

Moss,R. 1987. Demography of capercaillie *Tetras urogallus* in north-east Scotland. 11 Age and sex distribution. Ornis Scandinavica 18, 135-140.

Mutch,W.E.S., Lockie,O.J.D. & Cooper,A.B. 1976. The red deer in South Ross: a report on wildlife management in the Scottish Highlands. Department of Forestry and Natural Resources, University of Edinburgh.

Newton,I. 1979. Population ecology of raptors. T.& A.D.Poyser, Calton.

Nixon,C. 1992. A pilot study on the age structure and viability of the Mar Lodge Pinewoods. Report to SNH NE Region, NE/92/206.

Osborne,B.C. 1984. Habitat use by red deer *Cervus elaphus* and hill sheep in the west Highlands. J.App.Ecol.21, 497506.

Pearson, The Lord. 1991. Why green can be red. The Field, May.

Phillips,J., Watson,A. & MacDonald.A. 1993. A muirburn code. Scottish Natural Heritage, Battleby

Ratcliffe,P.R. 1984a. Population dynamics of red deer *Cervus elaphus* in Scottish commercial forests. Proceedings of the Royal Society of Edinburgh, 82B, 291-302.

Ratcliffe,P.R. 1984b. Population density and reproduction of red deer in Scottish commercial forests. Acta Zool. Fenn., 172, 191-192.

Ratcliffe,P.R. 1987a. Distribution and current status of Sika Deer *Cervus nippon* in Great Britain. Mammal Rev.17(1), 39-58.

Ratcliffe,P.R. 1987b. The management of red deer in the commercial forests of Scotland related to population dynamics and habitat changes. D.Phil.thesis, University of London.

Ratcliffe,P.R., Hall,J. & Allen,J. 1986. Computer predictions of sequential growth changes in commercial forests as an aid to wildlife management, with reference to red deer. Scottish Forestry, 40, 79-83.

Red Deer Commission Annual Reports. HMSO, Edinburgh.

Red Deer Commission 1990. Evidence to Agriculture Select Committee. In: Land Use & Forestry. HMSO.

Ritchie,J. 1920. The influence of man on animal life in Scotland. Cambridge University Press.

Scottish Natural Heritage. The National Countryside Monitoring Scheme for Scotland: Phase 1 : 1940s - 1970s. *In press.*

Staines,B.W. 1970. The management and dispersion of a red deer population in Glen Dye, Kincardineshire. PhD thesis, University of Aberdeen.

Staines,B.W. 1977. Factors affecting the seasonal distribution of deer *Cervus elaphus* at Glen Dye, north-east Scotland. Ann.appl.Biol., 87, 495-512.

Staines,B.W. 1978. The dynamics and performance of declining populations of red deer *Cervus elaphus*. J.Zool.Lond.,184, 403-419.

Staines,B.W. & Crisp,J.M. 1978. Observations on food quality in Scottish Red Deer *Cervus elaphus* as determined by chemical analysis of the rumen contents. J.Zool.185, 253-259.

Staines,B.W., Crisp,J.M. & Parish,T. 1982. Differences in the quality of food eaten by red deer *Cervus elaphus* stags and hinds in winter. J.Appl.Ecol., 19, 65-77.

Staines,B.W. & Welch,D. 1984. Habitat selection and impact of red *Cervus elaphus* and roe *Capreolus capreolus* deer in a Sitka spruce plantation. Proceedings of the Royal Society of Edinburgh, 82B,303-319.

Staines,B.W. & Ratcliffe,P.R. 1987. Estimating the abundance of red and roe deer and their current status in Great Britain. In: Mammal Population Studies. Ed.S.Harris. Symp.Zoo.Soc.Lond. 58, 131-152.

Staines,B.W. & Welch,D. 1989. An appraisal of deer damage in conifer plantations. In: Deer and Forestry. Ed.R.McIntosh. ICF. Edinburgh. pp.61-76.

Staines,B.W. & Scott,D. 1992. Recreation and red deer: a preliminary review of the issues. Report to the Countryside Commission for Scotland, R3/1/114/RH/KS.

Staines,B.W.,Balharry,R.,Farquharson,A.,Jenkins,D,& Racey,P. 1992. Red deer and the natural heritage. Scottish Natural Heritage, NE Region draft policy document.

Steven,H.M. & Carlisle,A. 1959. The native pinewoods of Scotland. Oliver & Boyd, Edinburgh & London.

Stewart,L.K. 1988. Deer in Scotland. In: The Changing Scene. Red Deer Commission, Inverness.

Sykes,J.M. 1992. Caledonian pinewood regeneration: progress after sixteen years of enclosure at Coille Coire Chuilc, Perthshire. Arboricultural Journal, 16, 61-67.

Tjernberg, M. 1983. Prey abundance and reproductive success of the golden eagle *Aquila chrysaetos* in Sweden. Holarctic Ecology, 6,17-23.

Watson,A. 1976. Food remains in the droppings of foxes *Vulpes vulpes* in the Cairngorms. J.Zool.,Lond. 180,, 495496.

Watson,A. 1983. Eighteenth century deer numbers and pine regeneration near Braemar, Scotland. Biol.Conserv., 25,289-305.

Watson,A. 1989. Land use, reduction of heather, and natural tree regeneration on open upland. ITE Ann.Rept., HMSO, London.

Watson,A. 1993. Defects of fencing for native woodlands. Native Woodlands Discussion Group Newsletter No 18, pp.5355.

Watson,A. & Staines,B.W. 1978. Differences in the quality of wintering areas used by male and female red deer *Cervus elaphus* in Aberdeenshire. J.Zool.,186, 544-550.

Watson,A., Payne,S. & Rae,R. 1989. Golden eagles *Aquila chrysaetos* land use and food in northeast Scotland. Ibis, 131, 336-348.

Watson,J., Langslow,D.R. & Rae,S.R. 1987. The impact of land-use changes on Golden Eagles in the Scottish Highlands. CSD Report No.720. Nature Conservancy Council, Peterborough.

Watson,J., Rae,S.R. & Stillman,R. 1992. Nesting density and breeding success of golden eagles in relation to food supply in Scotland. J.Anim.Ecol., 61, 543-550.

Watson,J.,Leitch,A.F. & Rae,S.R. in press. The diet of Golden Eagles *Aquila chrysaetos* in Scotland.

Weirsema,G.J. 1974. Observations on the supplementary winter feeding of red deer on an estate in the Central Highlands of Scotland. Unpubl. MSc., Agric. Univ. Wageningen.

Welch,D. 1971. Seasonal variation in herbivore use of different range types. In: Range Ecology Research, Glenfeshie Monitoring of Vegetation and Grazing Use. pp.9-11. The Nature Conservancy, Edinburgh.

Welch,D., Scott,D. & Staines,B.W. 1992. Study on effects of wintering red deer on heather moorland: report of work done April 1992-November 1992. Report to SNH, 07/91/F2A/218.

Whitehead,G.K. 1972. Deer of the World. Constable. London.

Whitehead,G.K. 1964. The Deer of Great Britain and Ireland. Routledge and Kegan Paul, London.

Wigan,M. 1991. The Scottish Highland Estate: preserving an environment. Swan Hill Press, Shrewsbury.

Youngson,R.W. 1970. Rearing red deer calves in captivity. J.Wildl.Mgmt, 34, 467-470.